HOW DOES YOUR ZODIACAL SIGN INFLUENCE YOUR HEALTH?

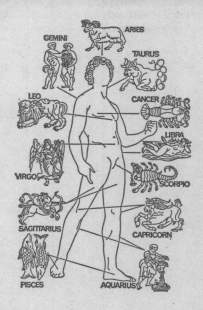

Each zodiacal sign rules a particular portion of your body. The sign under which you were born, and the dominance of different planets at various times of the year influence your fitness—or your susceptibility to specific ailments . . .

(continued on following page)

HERE ARE JUST A FEW OF
YOUR STRENGTHS AND WEAKNESSES
BASED ON YOUR ZODIACAL SIGN:

ARIES (March 21—April 19)

Governed by a fire sign which rules the head, produces many "human dynamos" who burn energy fast.

TAURUS (April 20—May 20)

The most fixed and determined sign of the zodiac, rules the neck, cerebellum, and thyroid gland. Taureans frequently need extra iodine.

GEMINI (May 21—June 21)

Nervous system & digestive processes easily affected by tension. Betony herb & nerve root helpful.

CANCER (June 22—July 21)

Rules muscular action of stomach. Cinnamon bark & ginger root act against digestive ailments.

LEO (July 22—August 21)

Ruled by the sun which in turn rules the heart, blood circulation, right eye in males, left in females.

VIRGO (August 22—September 22)

Inclined to follow dietary fads. Susceptible to digestive tract diseases.

LIBRA (September 23—October 22)

Generally graceful, well-shaped bodies, but subject to kidney ailments.

SCORPIO (October 23—November 21)

Rules procreation, reproduction and elimination. Slippery elm & cramp bark valuable herbs.

SAGITTARIUS (November 22—December 21)

Rules hips and thighs. Susceptible to overweight in these areas. (See special diets for overweight Sagittarians.)

CAPRICORN (December 22—January 20)

Ruled by Saturn which rules the skin, skeleton, hearing, gall bladder and part of the intestine.

AQUARIUS (January 21—February 19)

Especially intuitive. Rules by fixed air sign. Susceptible to lower leg sprains, varicose veins & broken ankles.

PISCES (February 20—March 20)

Sign of cosmic consciousness and the house of Karma. Susceptible to somnambulism, drug addiction & poison.

Your Astrological Guide to Health & Diet

Carroll Righter

BANTAM BOOKS · TORONTO · NEW YORK · LONDON

*This low-priced Bantam Book
has been completely reset in a type face
designed for easy reading, and was printed
from new plates. It contains the complete
text of the original hard-cover edition.*
NOT ONE WORD HAS BEEN OMITTED.

YOUR ASTROLOGICAL GUIDE TO HEALTH & DIET
*A Bantam Book / published by arrangement with
G. P. Putnam's Sons*

PRINTING HISTORY
*G. P. Putnam's Sons edition published October 1967
Bantam edition published March 1968*

*Bantam Books are published by Bantam Books, Inc., a subsidiary
of Grosset & Dunlap, Inc. Its trade-mark, consisting of the words
"Bantam Books" and the portrayal of a bantam, is registered in the
United States Patent Office and in other countries. Marca Registrada.
Bantam Books, Inc., 271 Madison Avenue, New York, N.Y. 10016.*

PRINTED IN THE UNITED STATES OF AMERICA

To Mary G. Roebling
a great lady
a distinguished American
and my friend

Contents

Introduction

Before man learned to sharpen a spear or fashion a slingshot with which to supplement his meager diet, he subsisted on plant life: berries, leaves, nuts, roots and the bark of trees. Experimenting with anything he could find, he learned that many were healthful and some were deadly. The birds and the wild beasts were his teachers as well, and he learned to shun the sumac and the root of the muscal cactus, noting that animals and birds would eat one small spongy plant but avoided other deadly ones that had a similar appearance.

Through experiment and observation man learned to eat. He came to learn that some foods merely satisfied his hunger, that some would ease the cramp in his stomach, some made him feel warm when he was chilled by cold and dampness, some made him relaxed and drowsy, and others cooled him when he burned with fever.

History does not record when man first ate a sprig of mint or the sassafras bark clawed from a tree or the wild onion dug from the earth. But whether by gesture or in some long-forgotten tongue, the earliest awareness of what to eat was passed on, from age to age, through immeasurable periods of time until man began to record on stone and later on wood and papyrus what he had learned about food.

Man's first discoveries and experiences relating to food (and survival) are indeed rooted in prehistory; likewise is the conception of astrology. The practice of medicine is also one of the most ancient of all arts. Many questions about ancient man will go forever unanswered, but archaeologists and anthropologists have learned from studying artifacts and carvings on stone that astrology and medicine were practiced as long as recorded history—and that these two arts went hand in hand.

Early man studied the heavens, noting the patterns of the stars, discovering that only a very few moved and the rest were always in the same place. He saw the huge ball of fire rise up over the hill in the morning, climb up higher and higher until it was directly over him and then as slowly sink out of view on the other side.

He also became aware that it had another path. At one position the buds formed on the trees, plants sprung from the earth and animals gave birth to their young. There followed a time of heat; the berries ripened, seed pods formed and the young animals grew to maturity. And then a period when the cold winds blew; the leaves dropped from the trees, plants withered and the fur on the animals grew thick. Over and over the pattern repeated itself until man began to plan his life by this strange cycle.

There was another body in the heavens that moved swiftly and changed in shape from a thin silver crescent to a full round circle of light and then would disappear completely. How long man watched and studied before he became aware of the influences of that body: the rise and fall of the water where the ocean met the land, even the behavior of the wild beasts. The position in the sky of the huge ball of fire and the change in shape of the silver crescent, these things seemed to affect all life.

A time came when he looked to the heavens when a child was born. Was it a time when the first leaf buds appeared, or was it a time when the days were cold and the fruit had dropped from the trees? Was it a time when the faint outline of the moon was visible, or was it a time when that circle was filled with light?

Early man was beset by disease and wounded by wild beasts. In his quest for surcease from these tribulations he turned to the things with which Nature had provided him, namely, plants and herbs. (This connection between the plant and the disease later became known as the Doctrine of Signatures.)

As with his experiments in finding nourishment for his body, there is little doubt that this search was a method of trial and error, but all ancient folklore confirms the fact that he did succeed in finding a great many amazing remedies. Because of the simplicity of his language, he named them according to the disease or the part of the body for which they were used. There was boneset, pleurisy root, wound wort, feverfew, campbark, scurvyroot, liverwort, lung wort, bruise wort, balm, heal-all—to name a few.

Along with his experiments in the use of herbs he began to notice a correlation between the herb, the disease and the position of those planets whose course he could follow. Countless years of observation and study followed, with man noting how the tendencies toward certain weaknesses among people who had been born at a time when the sun was in one of the groups of stars (constellations) differed from those who had been born at a time when the sun was at a different position and in another group.

In all tribal communities, because one man can do something better than his neighbor, he is the one chosen for that particular task. So it was in ancient tribes: the man who knew more about the effects of the heavenly bodies and was also the most proficient in the preparation of herbs for medicinal purposes became the astrologer-herbalist for that tribe or community.

Ever progressing in civilization, through ages of time and history, in whichever locality his birth or nomadic spirit had placed him, through disasters of nature or war between tribes, man carried the concepts of the first science, astrology (star-speech), and with it the first rudiments of medicine.

Astrological lore is very old, and the extensive knowledge that the ancient Egyptians, Babylonians, Chaldeans and Assyrians had concerning astrology and medicine was gained because of the belief in the divine influence of the heavenly bodies. The fundamental sequence of the seven basic planets (namely, sun, moon, Mercury, Venus Mars, Jupiter and Saturn) was established in Chaldea and still survives today. (The outer planets were unknown at that time, although some evidence has been uncovered that the planet Uranus was known in early times and merely rediscovered in the eighteenth century.)

There are several extraordinary scientific facts about this sequence which exhibit the unique perception of the ancient Mesopotamian astrologers in both astronomy and chemistry. A 4,000-year-old tablet in the British Museum lists the herbs used in Assyria and contains a note referring to "the Ancient Rulers before the Flood."

The ancient Egyptians were well versed in the science of astrology in its relation to astronomy and medicine. Their list of herbals was extensive, including astringents, aromatics, calmatives, cathartics, diuretics, expectorants, stimulants, sedatives, tonics, vermifuges and vulneraries. Records from early Egypt confirm that the astrologer-herbalist would first cast the horoscope and then diagnose the disease, after which he would prescribe the medication. (Licorice was found in the 3,000-year-old tomb of King Tutankhamen. Perhaps old King Tut had suffered from a bad cough and wanted to be sure of his medicine, licorice being an expectorant ruled by Gemini, which in turn ruled the lungs.)

From Chinese folklore dating back thousands of years, we find that they, too, used astrology and its principles in the selection and use of herbs for medicine.

In some countries of the Far East today doctors are paid in advance for keeping their patients in good health. Their use of astrology, i.e. the birth chart and the progressions to follow, indicating the health tendencies, assists them in their diagnoses and they can thus advise as well as prescribe for the indicated weakness.

The Romans, adept in the use of astrology (as witnessed by the numerous allusions to the science in the writing of their historians and philosophers), also had a vast knowledge of the science in its connection with herbs and medicine. Pliny mentioned herbs and "their signatures" some 2,000 years ago. To the list of herbs indigenous to their own empire they sought to add others whose value had been attested to by the Greeks and Arabs.

The Druids of Celtic Great Britain, Gaul, and probably all Celtic peoples, have attracted much attention because of their religious rituals. Although much of their learning was lost during the Dark Ages, some records of their knowledge of the occult and herbal medicine were preserved. Mistletoe, cut with a golden sword to ensure its "purity," was administered to cast out "evil spirits." Or, in slightly more modern phraseology, a clean instrument was used to obtain the berries and leaves with which to make a medicine for a certain malady.

The Arabs traded in spices from India in the twelfth century. Spices were much in demand, not only for flavoring but also for their medicinal value, and before the desire for conquest sent ships around the world, trading vessels called at every open port for the spices from India and tea from China. (Tea was mentioned in Chinese literature dating back to the third century A.D. as being used not only for its stimulating but also its astringency properties.) For thousands of years saffron has been praised for its medicinal qualities. In ancient time it was even used as a means of exchange because of its great value.

From earliest recorded history the clay tablets from Assyria, the ancient tombs of Egypt, relics of early Mayan culture in Central America, ancient Chinese literature—all aver their knowledge of astrology and the use of herbs in the treatment of disease.

Hippocrates, the "Father of Medicine" (460–377 B.C.), required that his students study astrology, stating, "The man who does not understand astrology is to be called fool rather than physician." The Arabs brought together the Graeco-Egyptian astrology of Ptolemy, ancient Chaldean scientific knowledge and Hindu methods from India. Through the Middle Ages and the Renaissance up to modern times, men whose names have become synonymous with the arts and sciences have proclaimed the value of astrology.

Geoffrey Chaucer (1340–1400), the "Father of English Poetry," write "Treatise on the Astrolabe" in order to teach astrology to his young son at Oxford. "Every one of the twelve signs hath respect to a certain part of the body of man, as Aries governs thy head and Taurus thy neck and thy throat, etc."

Jerome Cardan, the most spectacular physician of the early sixteenth century, was also an astrologer.

Some of the first books to be printed from movable type were herbals, in Latin, German and English. Among the notable ones is *Herball*, by John Gerard (1545–1612). In the seventeenth century William Cole wrote, "Herbs should be gathered at the Full Moon as the juice contained was the most plentifully stored at that time." Nicholas Culpeper (1616–1684) wrote in *Semliotica Uranica:* "The admirable Harmony of the Creation could be seen in the influence of the stars upon Herbs and Body of Man."

Following these there have been hundreds of herbals printed in every country in the world, including America.

In August 1962, the planet Uranus entered the zodiacal sign Virgo (the natural sixth house of health). It will continue its passage through this sign until June 1969. But "coming events cast their shadows before": we began to notice the effects of this particular transit a few years previous to the actual entry. There has been a renewed interest in the use of natural foods and herbs for nutrition, and in the treatment of disease to replace the synthetic vitamin pills. It has brought to light the dangers of the commercial pesticides.

From a leading medical journal, the following: "Modern science is now reevaluating many of the old-time botanicals and their use, searching jungles and distant places to seek remedies of aboriginal races." From *Preventive Medicine and Hygiene:* Cloves have "very marked antiseptic powers and are valuable preservatives."

Many doctors who have scoffed at the idea of astrology as a science and at its value in determining health tendencies may well look back to Hippocrates. Do not be surprised to see astrology playing an ever greater part in the New Medicine.

The next time you are given a prescription, look at the ℞ in the corner. This is a modern form of an ancient astrological symbol, an invocation to Jupiter to use his good offices toward a cure.

The body is an intricate and complex chemical factory. It separates the food elements and distributes them (via that unique conveyor belt, the digestive system) to the proper places. To build a strong and healthy body from infancy and to keep it in good health necessitates proper food, fresh air and exercise. Food must provide all the required vitamins and minerals. Certain elements are necessary for growth, some for self-repair, some to aid digestion, and others, by their fortifying qualities, to protect us from disease. We eat to live, to obtain energy and to provide pleasure.

Plants take sustenance from the soil, air and water, and within themselves form the chemical compounds necessary to the human body. We cannot eat iron ore to provide the iron we need, nor can we dig a vitamin from the earth, so we must depend on nature's factory, the plant, to supply us with these elements. The herb can be a food, a flavoring, a source of vitamins and minerals, a stimulant or a sedative. Although herbs were man's drugstore for thousands of years, not until science discovered the vitamin and mineral content of different foods was he aware of their full value.

In years gone by man's diet was limited largely to the supply in his locality, but now, with refrigerated and speedy transportation facilities, it is possible to get fresh fruits and vegetables almost everywhere. The best spices from India and the Far East, the best herbs from Europe and the Middle

East are available in every community. The usage of many of them has come to us from the place of their origin, but man has also experimented with combinations of herbs and spices from different countries. These blends are both delectable and healthful. The decoctions of herbs are the basis of many of our modern medicines.

All food products have a relationship with the signs and the planets. One ruled by a certain planet or sign may have a higher specific vitamin or mineral content; another may contain several in combination and therefore be more complex in rulership. The astrologian compares the horoscope with the food product and is thus able to determine the especial requisites of the native and the compensating dietary supplements.

Each zodiacal sign encompasses a definite body area, and rulership over the organs and members of the body is given to the planets. Each sign has physical, mental and emotional characteristics that have much bearing on the physiological and also the pathological tendencies of the ruling planet. The ruling planet in turn bestows a certain individual temperament upon the native according to his birth sign.

PLEASE NOTE: The reader is cautioned against self-medication and is urged to consult with a physician before engaging in a dietary program or in the use of any herbs, vitamins, minerals or medicinal elements referred to in this book. The author of this work is an astrologian, not a physician.

The author expresses his appreciation to Mr. Mervin Houser and Mrs. Estella Piffl for their great help and encouragement.

The
Twelve
Signs

Aries

(March 21–April 19)

RAM

THE FIRST SIGN of the zodiac is Aries, for all those born between March 21 and April 19. Aries stands for action. You are the pioneer, always seeking new fields of endeavor; competent and confident, you have the power to rise above adversity. Mars, your ruling planet, gives you a vast amount of energy. You are the human dynamo. As an Aries native you are starting a new cycle of existence, of experience and, if you so desire, advancement toward the ultimate goal of perfection. You are in a hurry to get on with it.

Development is mental, physical and emotional. Ariens have become the pioneers in numerous educational and entertainment fields. You desire knowledge for its value, not for display; imaginative and enthusiastic, you will step boldly into areas where angels fear to tread, or have probably never even heard of. Because you envision a project as a reality, you are apt to become bored with the idea long before completion. To fulfill the portents of your sign, you would do well to practice patience and perseverance. Ideas are born: the finished product requires work. There was only one great unfinished symphony; all other masterpieces of music, art or

11

literature have been the result of tedious labor. Nourish your idea, tend it patiently and watch it grow; only then will you develop stability and enjoy the thorough satisfaction of a job well done.

Physical activity, for which you have a natural inclination, will counteract any nervous tension caused by mental fatigue and the resulting digestive upsets. Sufficient rest is important; just a few moments of complete relaxation of both mind and body will do wonders for you. Being endowed with excellent recuperative powers, you have only to use moderation in all activities.

The emotional characteristics of a sign have an impact on both the mental and physical health. Ariens have a tendency to be excitable and quick-tempered; interference with their point of view brings quick response. You, as an Arien, with your abundance of ideas, your perception of detail, have the ability to achieve the heights of perfection and fulfillment.

Food, the proper food, is of the utmost importance. Our health tomorrow, our physical health and therefore to a great extent our mental and emotional health, depend on what we eat today.

You, as an Arien, like good food, but it is not as important to you as it is to some of the other signs; you often pay little attention to what you eat. I have known Aries natives who were reluctant to sit long enough to eat a proper meal. If there was a complete meal in pill form, an Arien would most likely be the first to try it. Being a fire sign, you burn up energy—supplied by vitamins and minerals—as a furnace consumes fuel. These essential elements must be replaced.

Certain diseases are peculiar to each zodiacal sign. Ariens may suffer headaches, vertigo, fevers, neuralgia, cerebral congestion, eye afflictions, eruptions, especially on head and face, inflammation, insomnia and wounds.

Although the sixth house, governing the processes of absorption, assimilation and peristalsis, is your weak house, your system usually will absorb only what it needs; therefore, overweight is seldom a problem. Nevertheless, it is advisable that you know the food elements your system requires—those which, because of your sign and planet ruler, must be replenished daily and those which may be lacking in your particular chemical make-up.

Protein is essential for all signs. It is found in meat, including the vitamin-carrying organs (liver, kidneys, etc.), in fish, nuts (especially raw nuts, not the roasted), in eggs, cheese, mushrooms, and in the legumes (dried soy, kidney, navy beans, etc.). Because Aries rules most of the spices—onions, garlic, ginger, pepper, chili powder, curry and mustard—the Arien may prefer a bowl of chili or a good curry to supply his protein.

The Arien must not forget to drink plenty of water, as Aries rules hydrogen, and Libra (the sign opposing Aries in the zodiac) rules oxygen. For good health the Arien must include other vitamins and minerals. Study the following list carefully and vary your diet according to your particular needs. And consult your physician.

ESSENTIAL VITAMINS*

Vitamin A: for night vision, functioning of cells of skin and mucous membrane

SOURCES

Milk, cheese, butter, fish oils, green-leaf vegetables (especially escarole), yellow vegetables (carrots, sweet potatoes), okra pods, watercress, lettuce, alfalfa herb, fruits with yellow flesh

Vitamin B1 (Thiamine): for growth, especially children and for maintaining normal appetite; gland and nerve vitamin

Whole grains, wheat germ, eggs, liver, walnuts, peanuts, peas, beans (dried), lentils, mushrooms, cabbage, asparagus

Vitamin B2 (Riboflavin): for development of red blood cells

Green-leaf vegetables (turnip greens, beet tops, mustard greens, broccoli, lettuce), liver, kidneys, apples, oranges, pears

Vitamin C (Ascorbic acid): for healthy teeth, gums; aids bone injuries

Apricot, orange, lemon, tomato, pineapple; vegetables, watercress, parsley, spinach, cabbage, onions, red peppers, etc.

ESSENTIAL MINERALS*   SOURCES

Iron: for vitality; the vehicle of oxygen in the blood

Lettuce, spinach, radishes, onions, ripe olives, watercress, rice bran, asparagus, romaine, strawberries

* See last chapter for complete list of foods containing essential vitamins and minerals.

The addition of carefully selected herbs and spices to any food—raw salads, cooked vegetables or meats, desserts (and an herb tea occasionally to replace either regular tea or coffee) —will not only enhance the flavor, but will provide an additional source of vitamins and minerals. Some of the herbs and spices which are ruled by Aries or Mars, or by your opposing sign Libra and which may be of special benefit in providing these essentials are the following:

> Paprika: Vitamins A, C, and P
> Watercress: Vitamins A, C, and D, magnesium, fluorine, sodium, iron
> Wheat germ (Libra): Vitamins B₂ and D
> Onions (raw): Vitamins C and D
> Peppers: Vitamins C and D
> Horseradish: Vitamin C
> Chives: Vitamin C, calcium, iron, sodium
> Garlic: Vitamin D, fluorine, sulphur, phosphorus
> Nettle: Calcium, potassium, sodium, iodine, sulphur
> Plantain: Calcium
> Sorrel: Calcium
> Table salt: Chlorine
> Parsley: Iron, magnesium
> Yellow dock: Iron
> Strawberry leaves: Iron
> Irish moss: Iron, sulphur
> Caraway seeds: Phosphorus
> Walnut leaves: Potassium
> Broom tops: Sulphur
> Sesame: Vitamin E
> Cumin seed: Vitamin A, calcium, iron
> Coriander seed: Vitamin A, calcium, iron

A sixteenth century proverb was: "In pottage without herbs there is neither goodness nor nourishment." With your tray of fresh vegetables add sliced onion and green pepper rings, tiny whole or shoe-string raw beets, and try a dash of oregano on the tomatoes. If raw onions don't agree with you, try them baked, or the milder chives, garlic or garlic salt. Try watercress and mustard-leaf sandwiches. Add a dash of thyme to soup. To green beans add tomato sauce and a little garlic salt. Try horseradish or mustard with meat. Add a pinch of curry powder to cream sauces for chicken, turkey, shrimp, beef or lamb.

Herb teas have flavor, aroma and are also beneficial—

from alfalfa tea to Yerba Santa, there is a tea for any time
of the day. Ginger tea is helpful for mild stomach upsets.
Hop tea is used mainly as a "bitter" to improve the appetite
and digestion, or taken warm before retiring it helps induce
sleep.

"The Lord hath created medicine out of the Earth: he
that is wise will not abhor them." Ecclesiastes XXXVIII:4.
In 1902 the following excerpt appeared in a cookery maga-
zine under the title "Medicine in Food": "There is a great
deal of truth in the old saying that 'the best doctor is the
cook.' The value of herbs and spices as medicine has never
been disputed." Rhubarb is a good tonic in the spring.
Parsley root (ruled by Libra, your opposing sign) is helpful
to the kidneys. Herbs that will assist in correcting some of
the planetary tendencies of your sign are the following:

For	Cooking herbs	Medicinal herbs
Head colds	Sage	Boneset
Catarrh	Anise seed	Marshmallow root
Watery eyes	Fennel	Camomile
Insomnia	Primrose	Valerian
Vertigo	Rue	Centaury

Some of the ancient beliefs concerning herbs ruled by
Aries may be of interest. If a house was considered haunted,
a bunch of garlic was hung over the door. The Egyptians
considered onions almost a holy herb and a must in most
of their cooking. The Chinese thought coriander seed would
confer immortality. To aid sleep, a pillow was filled with
hops, sprinkled lightly with a little alcohol to bring out the
soothing aroma. Horseradish has long been used as a warming plaster for stiff muscles or for rheumatism. Directions for
making a mustard plaster for the relief of chest colds appeared in all old-time herbals. From *Culpeper's Complete
Herbal* published in the early seventeenth century, these
notes: "Anemone (Mars ruled): juice from the mashed
leaves purgeth the head. Holy thistle (Mars and Aries): it
strengthens the attractive qualities in man."

Whole cloves have been used to sweeten the breath for
over 4,000 years. Spices are powerful germicides. In India,
where the heat is intense, the ancients discovered, by process of trial and error, that if meats were cooked in certain

spices, they would keep for days, and for weeks or even months if they were prepared in mustard oil. They used many combinations of spices, such as those which form the basis for curry.

Ginger root is chewed in the West Indies to alleviate the pain of toothache. According to William's *Plants of Zanzibar*, Swahili people burn curry leaf as incense to ward off bad dreams, evil spirits, etc. Garlic has been used for thousands of years; today it is known to have medicinal value. From an ancient herbal: "Garlic is a native of the East, but for its uses, is cultivated everywhere. Mars owns this herb. It was anciently accounted the poor man's treacle, it being a remedy for all diseases and hurts. It is held good in hydropic diseases, the jaundice, falling sickness; it kills the worms in children, takes away the spots and blemishes in the skin, eases pains in the ears, it purges the head and helps the lethargy."

The American Indians believed that herbs were necessary with certain foods. The best known was the root of the wild ginger. The oldest civilized people known in history—Assyrians, Egyptians, Persians and Babylonians—used dried herbs and the resin of trees and plants as incense and perfumes. The ancient Greeks and Romans kept urns filled with such botanicals to keep the air fresh and delicately scented.

Taurus

(April 20–May 20)

BULL

TAURUS IS A fixed, earth sign, ruled by the planet Venus, and therein lies the key to your physical, mental and emotional temperament and characteristics. In order to understand your sign, all these factors must be taken into consideration.

By quality your sign is symbolized by broad and fertile plains, warm with sunshine and bright with flowers.

In all signs there are contradictions, positive and negative factors, and your sign is no exception. It is up to you to use the best qualities you are endowed with by sign and ruling planet. You can be gentle and loyal or you can be quick-tempered and even malicious. You can be the epitome of grace, honesty, affection and depth of feeling—or you can be self-willed, obstinate and headstrong. You are usually quiet and self-controlled, but you may surprise those around you by a sudden outburst of temper.

Taurus is the most fixed and determined sign of the zodiac. You are inclined to be methodical in your way of doing things and wish to do everything well. Patient and deliberate, you

17

like to be sure of an idea or a situation before you act. It is best for you to think things out by yourself lest you become confused by the opinions and emotions of others. It may take you a long time to make up your mind, but once you have reached a decision or formed an opinion, you are apt to wear down any opposition by your tenacity. A certain amount of pride in one's self or in one's accomplishments is essential for success, but the Taurean would be wise not to let self-pride preclude fair judgment of others.

Many famous artists, actors, musicians and sculptors belong to your sign. Regardless of your own occupation, you have an appreciation for all things artistic and beautiful, and the desire to possess a Rubens or a collection of good music will stimulate you in your own field.

It might take you a little longer to master a subject in school or a profession, but you will remember what you have learned, and with your determination you can succeed in anything you try. Use your imagination along with your practical ability; do not be afraid of trying something new and different. Fixity of purpose is commendable, but to restrict one's self to certain ideas or conditions gives little opportunity for growth—either mental, spiritual or social. Your own way may be best for you, but mental blinders may deprive you of new experiences or opportunities. Explore diverse avenues of expression, be it in recreation or a hobby.

A key word of Taurus is finance, or financial condition. Many highly successful businessmen, financiers and bankers are born under your sign. In fact, there is hardly a field that you could not excel in. It is advisable that you use good judgment in matters of business or partnerships because at times you are stubborn, headstrong and quite set in your ways. With your charm and magnetism it takes only a minimum of effort on your part to elicit cooperation from others.

At times you may appear materialistic. You like to climb the ladder of success because success in one field of endeavor can bring you the good things from other pursuits. If not in an artistic sphere yourself, you often become a patron of the arts, enabling others to accomplish their goals and giving yourself the pleasure of contributing to the advancement of culture.

You are gracious and friendly, and your personality attracts many friends and acquaintances. Your amorous nature requires love and affection. Although you seldom analyze your own emotions, you are extremely responsive to the feelings of others. When once you have found your true love you are usually devoted and loyal. If, however, you do have a change of heart, you will put an end to the matter most decisively. No other sign can hang on to a personal relationship so resolutely or cast it away so completely.

You are fortunate in having Venus as your ruling planet, for she governs charm, beauty and good fortune. As with all planetary rulers, there are positive and negative characteristics. The positive ones—affectionate, friendly, amicable, harmonious, suave, moral and temperate—will be assets in any social or material venture. The negative ones—sensual, vain, lazy, superficial or self-centered—can only be liabilities. It is up to you to take full advantage of your most favorable attributes.

Attachments of all kinds are important to you—family, friends, environment or occupation. You prefer to hang on to people or situations as they are and are inclined to be quite possessive in any relationship. This attitude could limit your possibilities. It is not necessary to discard the old order to increase one's interest in the new. Enlarge your circle of friends, broaden your viewpoint, seize that sudden or unforeseen opportunity, and let the benefits from such expansion come to you.

In zodiacal anatomy each sign encompasses a certain part of the body and, together with the ruling planet, governs the organs within that area. The zodiacal signs also control the physiological functions and reveal the tendencies which might indicate physical infirmities. Taurus rules the neck, cerebellum, throat, pharynx, larynx, upper part of esophagus, thyroid gland, vocal cords, etc. Diseases peculiar to your sign affect this general area. They include diphtheria, goiter, glandular swellings in neck, polypus, laryngitis, quinsy, tonsillitis and strangulation. Self-indulgence could cause obesity or apoplexy. Consult your physician.

Misdirected energy will often cause a disease or endanger the chemical balance of the whole body. Practice moderation in all things. With strong signs in your fourth and sixth houses ruling stomach and intestines, you have an excellent appetite and good digestion; you enjoy good food but you will be healthier if you do not overeat. As Taurus and the second house govern the palate—the taste of things—you judge from a flavor point of view. This is not of any dietary importance if you follow a regimen best suited to your own needs. Taureans are inclined to be phlegmatic, but there is often a muscular tension and you are apt to gulp your food. Relax and dine at ease; try to eat more slowly. This will be better for you than after-dinner digestive pills.

Correct diet is of the utmost importance to any sign. Certain vitamins and minerals are naturally present in the body, others have to be replaced daily. If you have neglected to supply your body with its own particular needs, do it now. Food can be an ambrosia and still not contain the essentials, or it can be a simple salad and yet supply you with numerous healthful vitamins and minerals. Below is a list of foods containing the nutriments essential for you.

Taurus rules iodine, and the Taurean may need extra iodine. Venus, your ruling planet, may cause a lack of vitamins A and E, iodine and copper. Sources for these essentials

ESSENTIAL VITAMINS*	SOURCES
Vitamin A: for night vision, functioning of cells and mucous membrane	Alfalfa herb, escarole, chard, celery greens, okra pods, cream cheese, seafoods, eggs, milk, apricots, cherries, watercress
Vitamin B_1 (Thiamine): for growth and maintaining normal appetite	Kelp, okra, wheat germ, brown rice, avocado, lamb, lentils, etc.
Vitamin B_{12} for development of red blood cells	Alfalfa, kelp, dulse, bladderwrack
Vitamin B_2 (Riboflavin)	Kelp
Niacin: prevents pellagra	Alfalfa leaves, parsley leaves, watercress, wheat germ
Vitamin C (Ascorbic acid): for healthy teeth and gums; prevents scurvy	Citrus fruits: oranges, lemons, grapefruit, tomatoes, etc.
Vitamin D: for bones, anti-rachitis	Wheat germ, fish oils, seafoods, greens, etc.
Vitamin E: for fertility	Wheat germ, alfalfa, watercress, bean sprouts, kelp, etc.
Vitamins G, K: for process of blood clotting	Alfalfa herb, some legumes and vegetables
Vitamin P: (Rutin): strengthens tiny blood vessels	Herbs, buckwheat

* See last chapter for complete list and for list of essential minerals.

(they may be taken in juices) are apricots, apples, carrots, oranges, cucumbers, prunes, tomatoes, and spinach. Venus also rules apples, almonds, apricots, grapes, figs, peaches, wheat, roses and sweet-smelling spices.

The following cooking herbs will be helpful in curbing these planetary disease tendencies of Taurus:

Sore throat: Sage, fennel
Stiff neck: Chickweed
Goiter: Irish moss
Tonsillitis: Horehound

Earlier in this chapter it was noted that natives of your sign are intrigued by the taste of food. Why not use some of the Venus-ruled herbs listed below when preparing meats, fish, vegetables or salads? The flavor will be improved and they are an excellent source of vitamins and minerals.

Coltsfoot: Calcium, potassium, vitamin C
Sorrel: Calcium, sodium
Burdock: Iron (root), vitamin C (seed)
Strawberry leaves: Iron
Peppermint: Magnesium, potassium
Plantain leaves: Potassium
Yarrow: Potassium
Elder flowers: Hormones

Herb teas have been used for centuries; they are more healthful than Oriental teas. Beverage teas can be made from these Taurus- or Venus-ruled herbs: yarrow, pennyroyal, peppermint, thyme, tansy, balm, dittany, elder flowers, raspberry leaf, sage and spearmint.

The medicinal properties of many herbs have been recognized since earliest times, and Taurus—Venus-ruled herbs are used today for varying purposes in many parts of the world.

Calamus root is chewed by rustics in Europe and America to clear the voice and sweeten the breath. Coltsfoot is a predominant ingredient of British herb tobacco. Soapwort is used in many countries as a substitute for soap; it has many lather-forming qualities. Yarrow tea was a favorite medicinal brew of the old herbalists. It is used as a beverage mainly by Swiss mountaineers. *A Practical Guide for the Perfumer,* published in 1868, mentioned this about galangel: "The

Chinese prepare from it a very sweet essence, used to perfume the tea of the Emperor, and great officers of the Court." Pennsylvania farmers used to put mint in grain bags to discourage rodents. Darlington's *Flora Cestrica* recommends dittany tea as a pleasant beverage. The root of lovage, an aromatic plant, was once used in bath water in the belief that it would make one more lovable. An old European legend held that pillows stuffed with mugwort would reveal one's entire future in dreams. Vervain was generally included as an ingredient of "true love powders." Gerard's *Herball* notes that alder bark "is much used of poore country diers for the dyeing of coarse cloth, caps, hose and such like into a black colour, whereto it serveth well."

Several centuries before wonder drugs and out-patient clinics, herbals and home-remedy books gave instruction in the curative values of common herbs. One of the best-known herbals is by Culpeper, printed in the early seventeenth century. Here is his description of Venus-ruled herbs and their uses:

Bishop's weed: "It is hot and dry in the third degree, of a bitter taste: It provokes lust to purpose; I suppose Venus owns it."

Cudweed: "The juice of the herb is, as Pliny saith, a sovereign remedy against the mumps and quinsy: And further saith, that whosoever shall so take it shall never be troubled with that disease again."

Periwinkle: "It is a good female medicine and may be used with advantage in hysteria and other fits. The young tops made into a conserve is good for the nightmare."

Strawberries: "Lotions and gargles—defluctions of rheum in the throat."

Thyme: "An infusion of the leaves removes headaches, occasioned by inebriation."

Violets: "The flowers, fresh or dried—to lenify hoarseness of the throat."

Gemini

(May 21–June 21)

THE TWINS

GEMINI IS THE third zodiacal constellation, pictorially represented as the Twins, Castor and Pollux, and ruled by Mercury. Mercury, usually called quicksilver, is the only metal
that is liquid at normal temperature. Gemini is a mutable,
air sign. Mutable means "given to frequent change"; air, in
astrology, pertains to mentality. When you consider a few
key words of the sign and ruling planet, you get a general
idea of mental and emotional characteristics and, in turn, the
physical tendencies: Active, adaptable, curious, congenial,
inventive, versatile, literate and restless.

You have a keen and often brilliant mind, with a charming
personality and ready wit—the intellectual type who loves to
acquire knowledge. You can be truly learned or superficial,
eloquent or merely glib, a genius or what is known as a smart
operator, constructively active or a day-dreamer. When you
get a good idea—and a Gemini is intuitive—try to follow

23

through with it. Coordinate your idea with concentration and perseverance; the scatterbrain rarely achieves success.

You will attract a great variety of friends and acquaintances but it will be the brainy type that will attract you. You are usually well informed on a number of things because you like mental exchange, debate, and a good argument now and then—often with your best friend. You read and gather statistics in order to have plenty of evidence to support your opinions.

The desire to mingle with people will lead to quite an active social life. Being affable and congenial, you are often the life of the party. In affairs of the heart you are more likely to care for those with whom you have a mental rapport. You are affectionate and capable of much warmth and tenderness, but your mental moods often complicate your love affairs. If you have commitments or responsibilities in any type of partnership, do not let your penchant for diversified interests or companionships impair that relationship.

As a Gemini you are fond of travel; you like to go places and do things. If you are in a profession such as schoolteacher, secretary, accountant, or any job that keeps you more or less confined for a period of time, try to get away during your vacation. Unlike some signs, you are not content unless there is a little variety in your life. A change of scenery, meeting new people, will calm that inborn restlessness. You should, however, use such a period to good advantage.

Analyze yourself! You are industrious but you are inclined to scatter your energies; resolve to concentrate on one effort and to complete one project before going on to another.

Versatility is a key word of your sign, and manual dexterity one of your many talents. If you will but focus your brilliant mind on one creative impulse at a time, your skillful hands can perform the task of making it a reality. Composers and inventors are listed under your sign. If you are musically inclined, that inspirational idea could become a concerto if you will give it time to develop.

New ideas, new ways of simplifying old methods appeal to you. This inventive talent may be expressed in a less complicated form than an IBM machine; however, the Gemini male is adept at making gadgets, anything that will be more useful, less time-consuming than what is at hand. The Gemini female will give expression to her ingenuity in home décor.

Even the Gemini child likes to experiment. He may exasperate you because he is apt to be a walking question mark. Answer his questions intelligently; his eager mind will absorb much more than you may realize. He enjoys reading; provide him with good books. Good literature is important; words have meaning for him, and he likes to add new ones to his vocabulary. World geography will appeal to him as his interest in travel starts at an early age.

As a Gemini, you are intuitive, adaptable and, with your individual technique, often find reward in acting as a career. It is an arduous profession but well worth the effort it requires.

Indications show that your financial circumstances, like your moods, may vary from time to time. It is true that you like nice things. You like to be well dressed; a budget will help to curb that impulse to spend on something you do not really need.

Plan for the future in other matters as well as financial. You are impulsive; the moment you get a new idea you may want to drop everything and start anew. Think it over; weigh its merits. If it is worthy of consideration, then make your plans—but do not procrastinate; that mental impression will vanish unless you hold on to it.

Gemini natives are usually well qualified as accountants, secretaries, schoolteachers, lecturers, traveling salesmen, journalists, linguists, inventors, editors, orators and printers. This does not necessarily mean, however, that you will—or must—confine yourself to one.

In short, a Gemini is brilliant, dexterous, witty, subtle, sensitive, pleasing, literary, retentive. He can also be unprincipled, tale-bearing, conceited, forgetful, nervous, given to worry.

In zodiacal anatomy the sign Gemini rules the arms, shoulders, muscles and bones of arms and shoulders, lungs (including trachea and bronchii), thymus gland, upper ribs, capillaries and hands. Gemini and Mercury govern the air in the body and its circulation, nerve reflexes and the nerve functions in general, respiration and the sense of touch.

Your digestion in itself is good, but worry, restlessness and tension are harmful to your nervous system. This in turn impairs the digestive process, resulting in poor elimination.

Headaches, loss of memory, respiratory difficulties and

speech impediments often arise from nervous disorders. Afflictions to the sun sign (or ruling planet) often increase the tendency to a certain ailment. In determining disease tendencies, many factors must be taken into consideration: the functions of the organs, pathological traits (according to sign and ruling planet) and the diseases to which the native seems most susceptible. You should know where you might be more sensitive and act accordingly. Gemini is prone to bronchitis, pulmonary consumption, pneumonia, pleurisy, fractures of shoulders, arms and hands. Your sign also rules sensory communication and oxygenation of the blood. Impure blood or anemia will exhaust your natural vitality.

If you want to have the best chance of being healthier and living longer, build your body of the best materials and keep supplying it with all the elements it needs for replacement and repair. (The prudent reader will always confer with his physician.) Your active mind and roving feet require energy; this energy is supplied by the food you eat. Deep breathing helps.

A Gemini is not usually food-conscious. Your mind is more on where you are going, who you are going to see, the books you read or the discussions you love so well, rather than on a sumptuous meal. You might, however, be somewhat picky in your choice of food and limit your diet to the few things you really like, eating basically the same meals day after day. They may be good for you, but you may be limiting your vitamin and mineral supply, and eventually these elements must be replenished. It is much better to vary your diet, to learn the value of different foods and the essential elements they contain.

All vitamins and minerals are imperative to our well-being. Some are naturally present in the body, others must be added daily. You are in a sign governing the intelligence; use it! Study the various properties of different foods; know the ones you may lack and the vitamins you may need for your own disease tendencies. Vitamin balance is necessary to normal health, and mineral balance is necessary to the activity of vitamins; too much of one and not enough of another will only create further disorder.

Proteins supply heat and strength and replace worn-out tissue. As building foods, they are essential. Protein is found in meat, fish, eggs, cheese, nuts, whole grains and legumes.

You may prefer nuts to meat or meat to cheese; whichever will supply your protein need is up to your own taste and choice.

ESSENTIAL VITAMINS*	SOURCES
Vitamin A: for night vision, functioning of cells of skin and mucous membrane	Cheese, whole milk, butter, liver, fish oils, green-leaf vegetables, yellow vegetables, alfalfa herb, parsley, etc.
Vitamin B_1: (Thiamine): for growth	Yeast, whole grains, eggs, legumes, kelp, etc.
Vitamin B_2: (Riboflavin): for growth and nutrition	Green-leaf vegetables, milk, cheese, lean meats, whole-grain products
Niacin: prevents pellagra	Alfalfa leaves, parsley, wheat germ
Vitamin B_{12}: for growth factors, red blood cells	Alfalfa, kelp, liver
Vitamin C (Ascorbic acid): for teeth and gums; prevents scurvy	Citrus fruits, tomatoes, raw cabbage, etc.
Vitamin D: for bones and teeth; prevents rickets	Fish-liver oils, wheat germ, etc.
Vitamin E: for fertility	Wheat germ, lettuce
Vitamin K: necessary in process of blood clotting	Alfalfa herb, etc.
Vitamin P (Rutin): for tiny blood vessels	Buckwheat, paprika

ESSENTIAL MINERALS*	SOURCES
Calcium: for bones and teeth	Cheese, milk, arrowroot, and some vegetables
Fluorine: for teeth, hair, skin	Watercress, butter, fish, brown rice, etc.
Iodine: for thyroid, nervous tension	Seafood, kelp, some fruits and vegetables
Iron: for physical energy	Raisins, mushrooms, parsley, etc.
Magnesium: for gland secretion	Walnuts, bananas, okra, some berries, etc.
Phosphorus: for cells and nervous system	Watercress, lettuce, cheese, caraway seeds, licorice root (both Mercury-ruled)
Potassium: for muscles and body repair	Tomato, lettuce, turnips, celery, etc.

* See last chapter for complete list.

ESSENTIAL MINERALS*	SOURCES
Silicon: for connective tissue in body	Lettuce, asparagus, spinach, etc.
Sodium: for ligaments, resistance and endurance	Celery, spinach, oysters, etc.
Sulphur: helps to eliminate impurities	Kale, watercress, raw cabbage, chives, garlic, etc.

* See last chapter for complete list.

Mercury-afflicted natives may lack B complex, calcium, vitamin D; these are found in grapefruit, pineapple, rhubarb, parsley, watercress, liver.

Most vegetables contain multiple vitamins and minerals:

Celery: Vitamins A, B, C, E, and minerals, especially calcium.
Okra: Vitamin A, calcium, phosphorus, iron.
Radishes: Vitamins A, B, C, and minerals, especially iodine.
Ripe olives: Vitamin A, calcium, iron, riboflavin.

Mercury rules carrots, calamint, parsley, walnuts, filberts, and hazel nuts, as well as many herbs. Medicinal uses of some of these herbs are:

Calmatives: Fennel
Nervine: Valerian
Cathartic: Senna
Carminative: Caraway seed
Astringent: Maidenhair fern, bittersweet twigs
Vermifuge: Pomegranate rind
Emollient: Flaxseed meal
Stimulant: Summer savory herb
Expectorant: Elecampane root, licorice root, horehound herb, summer savory herb sauce

Man has used herbs as medicine since his earliest existence. Elecampane was mentioned by Pliny some 2,000 years ago. Licorice was found in the 3,000-year-old tomb of King Tutankhamen of Egypt, together with jewelry and art works. Parsley is one of the oldest known herbs. The Greeks and Romans used to form it into wreaths. Irish peasants used it to get rid of fleas. Also, an old Chinese name for parsley meant "kill flea." Albertus Magnus wrote in the Middle Ages that a decoction of valerian roots "restored peace and harmony between man and wife." It does have sedative qualities. Elecampane and maidenfern were used in witches' brews or "to sense the presence of witches."

Culpeper's Complete Herbal, published early in the seventeenth century, described these uses of Mercury-ruled herbs:

Bittersweet: "It is under the planet Mercury. It is good to remove witchcraft, both in man and beast, and all sudden diseases what-so-ever."

Dill: "Mercury hath dominion of this plant, therefore to be sure it strengthens the brain."

Elecampane: "One of the most beneficial roots nature affords for the help of the consumptive. It resists poison, pestilential fevers, even the plague itself."

Fenugreek: "Hot in the second degree and dry in the first —a decoction made first with dates and afterwards in syrup made with honey—cleanses the breast, chest and lungs."

Horehound (Black): "The leaves beaten with salt and applied to the wound, cures the bites of mad dogs. It is recommended against hysteric and hypochondriac affections."

Moonchild

(Also known as Cancer)
(June 22–July 21)

CHILD

THIS SIGN HAS a dual meaning. It denotes the crab with its hard-shelled exterior and soft inner body, moving slowly with feelers extended and with the habit of pulling itself back into its own shell for protection. Because of the characteristics of the sign, it is also said to represent the human breasts, signifying mother and home. The lower cup will gather and hold for children and family; the inverted cup signifies the quality of giving.

It is a water sign and ruled by the moon. In astrology, water represents anything that is fluid, emotional and psychic. Because of the influence of the moon, this sign is often changeable, subject to moods, impressions and occult forces. Water has a tendency to flow downward and needs another force to push it up. Some of the mental characteristics of your sign provide that force. You are imaginative and perceptive. Although of an emotional nature, you often have remarkable business ability. Being able to construct and reconstruct in your imagination helps you to be creative.

As either a male or female Moonchild you have a sixth sense when it comes to business, especially merchandising. You have a better sense of values than most signs; you are a cautious buyer and a shrewd trader. Perceptive of the needs of people, you also know where to obtain an item and the best way to sell it.

If, because of your emotional nature, you find yourself being somewhat visionary or even negative in your approach to a problem, remember that your sign has many positive qualities. Once you have distinguished between fact and fantasy, you should plan your course of action. You can be decisive without being impulsive. You are conscientious, but unnecessary brooding will not solve a matter. Strength of purpose and success depend upon your choice of attitude. You are industrious and persevering, whether in business for yourself or in the employ of another.

Sometimes, because of the planetary placements in a particular horoscope, the Moonchild native is not ambitious for himself, in which case he is apt to be instrumental in guiding the destiny of another. This, no doubt, stems from the tendency of the sign to see others as children and to help them.

Yours is the most domestic of all the signs. The concerns of home and family usually take precedence over all other matters. The average Moonchild is happier married than single and, regardless of where your business interests may take you, home is where the heart is. You like a comfortable, inviting home where you can gather your loved ones around you. It is often difficult for you to let them go, but you must remember that each individual must have some freedom of choice in the plans for his own future.

Love to you is a serious matter. You are devoted and loyal, but, being very sensitive, you are apt to feel hurt over the slightest misunderstanding.

Natives of your sign are successful in every profession or occupation. The intuitive quality of your sign helps you to understand what people want or need. Some Moonchild natives have artistic ability and excel in music, art, literature and drama. Others are inventors, merchants, designers, educators, scientists, and clergymen. Two American Presidents have been of this sign. It is interesting to note that Elias

Howe, a Moonchild, invented the sewing machine for his wife.

It often takes you longer to achieve success in the business world than some signs, but you have the tenacity to hold on. With your psychic faculties you are able to examine an undertaking in your mind, and the merchant often travels far and wide while sitting at his desk.

As a Moonchild you are imaginative and dramatic, and a goodly number of your sign have become sensitive and competent actors. You should, however, restrain that tendency to be so dramatic in your own imagination that you visualize conditions or situations that are nonexistent. You become so emotionally involved in the lives of family and friends that you cease to be objective. They will thank you for your sincere interest, but too much advice may be considered meddling in their affairs. You will feel that your good intentions have been rejected, taking it as a personal affront and becoming moody and very sorry for yourself.

In youth, those of your sign are imaginative and receptive. You may appear to be a dreamer, but knowledge soaks in and you have an unfailing memory. You like history, sea stories, tales of hero worship and fantasy. There is a tendency to be lethargic, and you may be moody and melancholy at times. In youth, as well as in later life, your extreme sensitivity will be a handicap. The slightest rebuke from a teacher you take to heart. You are versatile and should be encouraged in your ambitions. You are generally fond of home and parents, and family ties are very strong. You are conscientious, whether in school or home duties.

The female Moonchild is a sympathetic and protective woman, devoted to her family and solicitous for their welfare. She can be kind-hearted and self-sacrificing. On the other hand, she can be moody, changeable and possessive. As a teacher, especially nursery or kindergarten, home economist or interior decorator, she would be using her talents and, at the same time, stimulating her interest in problems and relationships beyond the confines of her home.

As one of the water triplicity, this emotional sign is concerned with the subject of growth, and the woman, by expanding her activities, will be more understanding of life as a whole.

The male of this sign is not always easy to live with. He loves his home, but is inclined to be critical and fussy. He may be the industrious type, concerned with providing for his family, or he may be lazy and self-indulgent. He is a devoted husband and father, not apt to stray from his own fireside, but he likes attention and usually expects everyone to listen to his troubles and cater to his needs, indulging in self-pity if he feels neglected. Characteristic of the sign, he can be dark and gloomy one moment, bright and sunny the next.

Generally speaking, the natives of this sign are interested in all phases of the occult and some are truly psychic, becoming mediums, prophets or clairvoyants.

In zodiacal anatomy this sign rules the stomach, breasts, lacteals, solar plexus, pancreas, epigastric region, diaphragm, thoracic duct and upper lobes of liver. It also controls the physiological functions of nutrition, body alchemy, absorption and the muscular action of the stomach. It thus becomes apparent that any irregularity in these functions will affect the regions ruled by the sign and, in turn, the general health.

Emotional upsets, resulting from lack of self-control, cause that "nervous stomach." When the stomach muscles become tense, the chemical process slows down and you become subject to various ailments. Your stomach can take a lot of punishment. You can burn it with hot soup and chill it with iced drinks and it will continue to function properly, but to ensure good health you should learn to control your emotions and to follow proper dietary rules. The moon, your ruling planet, returns to its radical position every four years from date of birth. By this movement, the affairs of home and health are periodically intensified. Note this pattern and take special care during such a period; you may be able to save yourself unnecessary ill health. Check with your physician regularly.

Natives of this sign love good food (they are usually very good cooks), and this often causes them to be overweight. Despondency, an emotional characteristic of a Moonchild, may lead to dipsomania. Self-control will eradicate these tendencies. Study the basic nutritional requirements and those that are specific to your sign.

ESSENTIAL VITAMINS*	SOURCES
Vitamin A: for night vision, cells of skin and mucous membrane; quickly dissipated	Butter, whole milk, liver, fish-liver oils, green-leaf vegetables, yellow vegetables, alfalfa herb, okra, etc.
Vitamin B_1 (Thiamine): for growth	Yeast, whole grains, kelp, legumes
Vitamin B_2 (Riboflavin): for growth and nutrition	Same as B_1
Vitamin B_{12}: prevents pernicious anemia	Liver, kelp
Vitamin C (Ascorbic acid): for teeth and gums, prevent scurvy; not stored in body, daily supply needed	Citrus fruits, tomatoes, baked potato, some herbs, raw cabbage (moon-ruled)
Vitamin D: for bones, teeth; prevents rickets	Fish-liver oils, egg yolk, wheat germ, watercress
Vitamin E: for fertility	Wheat-germ, lettuce, kelp
Vitamins K_1 and K_2: for blood clotting	Green-leaf vegetables, cabbage, spinach, cauliflower
Vitamin P (Rutin): strengthens tiny blood vessels	Paprika, lemon rind

ESSENTIAL MINERALS*	SOURCES
Calcium: for body structure	Watercress, milk (or buttermilk), cheese, cabbage, okra, lettuce, arrowroot, chives
Copper: for normal functions of body; assimilation of iron	Apricots, oysters, some nuts, molasses, shellfish
Fluorine: for teeth, hair, skin	Watercress, escarole, garlic, cabbage, whole oats
Iodine: for thyroid	Fish, kelp, radishes, etc.
Iron: makes red blood, prevents anemia, fatigue, etc.	Sorrel, lettuce, parsley, leeks, spinach, asparagus
Magnesium: gland and sex chemical	Tomatoes, dill, dandelion, celery, cabbage, rice bran
Phosphorus: for nervous system; prevents acidity	Kale, radishes, wheat bran, caraway seed, mushrooms, buttermilk, watercress
Potassium: for muscles; prevents hardening of arteries	Tomatoes, parsley, lettuce, celery, string beans

* See last chapter for complete list.

ESSENTIAL MINERALS*   SOURCES

Sodium: builds tissues, essential to repair; helps resistance — Celery, spinach, oysters, red beets, tomatoes, etc.

Sulphur: prevents infection, enlivens the system — Kale, watercress, horseradish, cabbage garlic

Silicon: for connective tissues, prevents nervous exhaustion — Lamb's lettuce, parsnips, asparagus, onions, spinach

* See last chapter for complete list.

Your sign and the moon rule; cabbage, carob pods (natural sugar), cucumbers, endive, lettuce, watercress, mushrooms, hyssop, purslane, pumpkins, rosemary, maple syrup.

Carob pods, an easily digested and nutritive botanical containing up to 50 percent natural sugar, may be eaten in place of high calorie-count desserts. Purslane is good for the digestion. Hyssop is a diaphoretic and often used in the relief of common colds. Lettuce and cabbage contain multiple vitamins and minerals. The mushroom has all the nourishment contained in meat. The moon may cause a lack of vitamin B complex and may affect water-salt balance; try vegetable juices: asparagus, carrot, celery and watercress or pineapple and coconut.

Celery seed is good for gastric disturbances; try a pinch in soup, or make a tea, using one teaspoonful to a cup of water. Peppermint tea is helpful for stomach disorders. Chickweed (moon-ruled) is a fine reducing herb and also a blood purifier. Brew as a tea (one teaspoonful to a cup). It also is a source of phosphorus. Cabbage, cucumbers, endive, lettuce and watercress (all moon-ruled) contain multiple vitamins and minerals.

Try whole brown rice with meat, fish or eggs. It is less fattening than potatoes and digests very quickly. For a soothing demulcent use slippery-elm bark or flaxseed for minor sore throat. Balm tea is excellent as a nervine. It gives temporary relief to the hypersensitive. Wintergreen tea is a pleasant beverage and more healthful than the Oriental teas.

A moon-ruled herb known as "Master of the Woods," used today in Germany to flavor May wine, was a good-luck charm of ancient Teuton warriors. They tucked a sprig of this dainty herb in their helmet or animal-skin mantle, believing it would assure success in battle.

In olden times, herbs and spices were considered nature's drugstore and herbalists prepared their own medicines. Herbals or home-remedy books listed these, their properties and which sign or planet governed them. *Culpeper's Complete Herbal,* first printed in the early seventeenth century, described many moon-ruled herbs. Here are some examples:

Adder's tongue: ". . . for the internal work of nature in the body of man, the apprehension, judgment, memory; the virtues retentive, digestive."

Brank ursine: ". . . the leaves being boiled and used in clysters, are excellent good to mollify the belly, and make the passage slippers."

Cabbages: ". . . This was certainly Chrysippus's god, and therefore he wrote a whole volume about them and their virtues, and that none of the least neither, for he would be no small fool . . . and honest old Cato, they say used no other physic."

Clary (wild): "A decoction of the leaves being drunk, warms the stomach. The seeds of it beaten to a powder, and drunk with wine, is an admirable help to provoke lust. It is a capital remedy for dimness of sight. . . ."

Cleavers: "It is a good remedy in the spring, to cleanse the blood and fitting it for that change of season that is coming. . . ."

Cucumbers: "There is no dispute to be made but that they are under the dominion of the Moon, though they are so much cried out against for their coldness, and if they were but one degree colder they would be poison. They are good for a hot stomach . . . the face being washed with their juice, cleanseth the skin. . . ."

Flag (Bastard water): "The spicy bitterness of the root bespeaks it a strengther of the stomach."

Poppy (white, or opium): "The syrup is a gentle narcotic, easing pain and causing sleep. . . . An overdose causes immoderate mirth or stupidity . . . giddiness of the head, deep sleep, cold sweats, and frequently death."

Purslane: "It stays hot and choleric fluxes of the belly. . . . It is good for pains in the head proceeding from want of sleep, or the frenzy."

Saxifrage: ". . . good for the colic and weakness of the stomach. . . ."

Watercress: "Watercress pottage is a good remedy to cleanse the blood in the spring. If any fancy not pottage, they may eat the herb as a salad."

Leo

(July 22–August 21)

LION

THE SIGN OF Leo is ruled by the sun, giver of life. The symbol of the sun is a circle with a dot in the center. The circle represents that which is infinite and boundless; the dot represents the heart of man, the central dynamo of the body. The sun, in astrology, stands for life, energy, vitality, authority and the real self. Leo is a fire sign, and as fire tends to move upward, so the natives of this sign strive to reach higher and higher. Fire gives warmth; the sun imparts light and radiance. It shines on one and all alike.

As a Leo, your strong individuality is based upon certain fundamental attitudes which color your thoughts, feelings and actions.

You think big; you aspire to the heights in your profession. Ability, ambition and personal magnetism usually help you to attain those heights. You can present such a forceful and dynamic pose that you floor any opposition. Keep in mind, however, that others may have ambition and yet lack some of the masterful qualities that you possess. No one will begrudge you your position or your fortune if you will show the consideration and reveal the magnanimity with which you are so naturally endowed.

Your generosity often exceeds your means. In this desire to help others or to bestow lavish gifts upon your family and friends you can be kind and self-sacrificing. Your motives are sincere, but the manner in which they are expressed is important, especially to the recipient. He will accept anything from the goodness of your heart, but will resent any ostentatious benevolence.

Although the tendencies of your sign are emotional and physical rather than mental, Leos reach the top in every profession. The list is long and many of the names are world known, for example George Bernard Shaw, Simon Bolivar, Henry Ford, Herbert C. Hoover and Dr. Charles Mayo.

Consider the versatility of these few Leos and how they expressed their true Leo qualities in bold and yet dignified procedure. Such natives of your sign should inspire each of you to use your own abilities and positive qualities to the fullest extent.

As the reader well knows, there are exceptions to every rule. To have been born under any sign, with its advantageous qualities and its professional tendencies, is no guarantee that you will reach the pinnacle of success. There are Leos who envision themselves as affluent members of an elite society, or as famous actors, writers or captains of industry, but who lack the ambition and the mental and physical fortitude necessary to energize these fantasies. They suffer from delusions of grandeur, expecting fame and fortune to fall into their laps without any persistent effort on their part.

Romance and entertainment are also represented by your birth sign. By nature you are affectionate, capable of intense feelings, somewhat aggressive and apt to be jealous. Your judgment in most matters is quite sound, but in affairs of the heart it is not always reliable. Certain signs are not as compatible with Leos as others. You deplore constant bickerings over small matters or the tendency of the natives of some signs to be frugal whereas you like to spend freely and lavishly. Such differences would not be conducive to harmony. You need love and affection and a partner who is in tune with your temperament.

You enjoy recreation and entertainment as a spectator or as a participant. Leos are strong-willed and can usually beat their way to the top in their particular field despite handicaps or obstacles. Their courage and optimism will carry them through when the going gets rough.

As a Leo, you have an active imagination which helps you to formulate new and original ideas, and you have sufficient coordination of mind and body to think and act almost simultaneously. These aptitudes are found in Leo-ruled athletes, dancers and entertainers.

You, as a Leo, are confident of your own worth and assume that others are aware of it also. You are a good leader but a poor follower. You have the natural charm and magnetism to influence others and to have them carry out your ideas.

Leo is a fixed sign; it bestows tenacity and determination. However, if you are domineering or if your self-confidence appears to others as a self-conceit, you will antagonize those you wish to impress. Your inborn generosity is one of your supreme virtues; let it extend to your relations with others. Show a genuine interest in their ideas and a willingness to cooperate in a common effort.

The sun rules the temperament of Leo natives, and it inclines the mind toward accomplishment. They do not give up easily, whether in the pursuance of business or beliefs. Idealistic by nature, we find many writers and newspapermen, born under this sign, who will fight for their principles, oblivious to criticism and without fear.

Unless the individual horoscope is heavily afflicted, the Leo, with his pleasing and magnetic personality, can be successful in business or in any occupation dealing with the general public. Being able to assume responsibility, he makes a reliable executive.

This sign is also a good placement for judges, government officials, brokers, bankers and foremen. The Leo usually has good earning possibilities; however, sudden success may give him a false sense of security and it would be wise for him to curb his extravagant tastes until he is firmly established and his financial condition stabilized. By using good judgment in all matters, Leos who achieve success will most often maintain it for the rest of their lives.

The Leo native should be cautious in all matters pertaining to gambling or speculation. He likes to take chances, but should remember that "easy come, easy go" is not conducive to financial security.

By using your positive qualities in all matters, you as a Leo should be able to realize your ambitions and enjoy a happy and productive life.

The Leo child exhibits the general characteristics of the sign. In games he is usually the leader and has a tendency to be bossy. He is quick-tempered, but usually forgives and forgets quite easily. He feels that he knows best about things in general; he is strong-willed and sometimes cruel.

If some of these less desirable tendencies are curbed in childhood, the Leo child will develop his more agreeable and altruistic characteristics. He is ambitious, enthusiastic, often inventive and he learns and profits from his own mistakes.

The Leo wife is an ideal mate for the ambitious and sophisticated man. She is a charming and gracious hostess, a good conversationalist when need be and often the leader in social groups. She is passionate in love and lavish in her affection for husband and family. Leonine women are often beautiful and enjoy an active and stimulating life.

The Leo husband is proud of his family and wants them to have the best of everything. He is generous, but he also likes to impress others and is very conscious of his standing in the community. He is devoted and loyal, but he demands respect and compliance with his wishes.

The vitality of Leo natives is usually strong, but they may overtax themselves by overwork in their eagerness to be successful. The physical constitution is also strong and they have excellent recuperative powers.

In zodiacal anatomy, Leo rules the heart, spinal column, with its marrow, especially the dorsal region and the spinal cord. The sun rules the heart, blood circulation, eyes in general, vital fluid, spleen, right eye in males and left eye in females, the back in general and spermic cells.

Diseases peculiar to the sun and to the sign Leo include diseases of the heart and arteries, spinal ailments, angina pectoris, palpitations, poor circulation, fainting spells, eye disorders, fevers, diseases of the spleen, sunstroke and throat trouble caused by heart condition.

As a Leo, you usually obtain complete nourishment from what you eat, so it is not necessary for you to consume great quantities of food. You enjoy being active, but you must take time to relax. The body needs proper and consistent upkeep

—the necessary amount of rest and food that provides the essential vitamins and minerals.

ESSENTIAL VITAMINS*	SOURCES
Vitamin A: for night vision, cells of skin, mucous membrane, anti-infective	Seafoods, liver, whole milk, eggs, dark green vegetables, yellow vegetables, fruits with yellow flesh, lamb, escarole, etc.
Vitamin B₁ (Thiamine): for growth; to maintain normal appetite	Whole grains, legumes, okra, kelp, walnuts (sun-ruled), alfalfa, rice (sun-ruled)
Vitamin B₂ (Riboflavin): for normal growth in children, nutrition for adults	Lean meats, green-leaf vegetables, milk, whole grains, raw salads, kelp, saffron (sun-ruled)
Vitamin B₁₂: To develop red blood cells	Liver, whole wheat, alfalfa, egg yolk, etc.
Niacin: prevents pellagra	Watercress, sea herbs, parsley, wheat germ, alfalfa
Vitamin C (Ascorbic acid): for teeth, gums; prevents scurvy; helps prevent common cold	Citrus fruits, tomatoes, cabbage, rose hips, parsley, watercress, oregano, marigold, strawberries, etc.
Vitamin D: for teeth, bones; prevents rickets	Fish-liver oils, seafoods, milk, wheat germ, greens, raw cabbage, coconut oil
Vitamin E: for fertility	Lettuce, dandelion leaves, kelp, wheat germ
Vitamin P (Rutin): strengthens tiny blood vessels	Buckwheat, paprika, German rue

ESSENTIAL MINERALS*	SOURCES
Calcium: for strong teeth and bones	Arrowroot, milk, cheese, kale, dill, lettuce, okra, dandelion, cabbage, spinach, watercress, etc.
Chlorine: blood purifier, normalizes heart action, helps make gastric juices	Oysters, cheese, tomatoes, celery, lettuce, buttermilk, etc.
Fluorine: for enamel on teeth, firmness of bones; eyes	Sea herbs and sea fish, whole oats, garlic, cabbage, beets, corn, brown rice, asparagus, etc.
Iodine: for thyroid	Shellfish, lettuce, radishes, squash, kelp, etc.

* See last chapter for complete list.

ESSENTIAL MINERALS*	SOURCES
Iron: important blood salt, for red blood cells, vehicle of oxygen in the blood	Sorrel, lettuce, leeks, onions, parsley, rice, bran, romaine, radishes, strawberries, dandelion, etc.
Magnesium: for glands	Tomatoes, dill, spinach, lettuce, carrot leaves, celery, kale, etc.
Nickel: for pancreas	Shellfish, bean sprouts, onions, garlic, fresh greens
Phosphorus: for teeth, bones; prevents paralysis, nervous condition	Radishes, kale, wheat bran, seafood, mushrooms, caraway seeds, sesame, cheese, cucumbers, etc.
Potassium: muscle builder, to repair body	Nearly all vegetables and legumes, mushrooms, molasses, peppermint, etc.
Silicon: for connective tissues; hair, nails, eyes, teeth	Lettuce, parsnips, asparagus, dandelion, horseradish, onions, spinach, cucumbers, etc.
Sodium: for tissue and ligaments; gives resistance and endurance	Celery, spinach, oysters, tomatoes, red beets, carrots, cheese, butter, chives, etc.
Sulphur: an antiseptic	Kale, watercress, garlic, dill, horseradish, turnips, etc.

* See last chapter for complete list.

Many of the essential vitamins and minerals are contained in foods ruled by your sign. The sun and Leo rule citrus fruits, cinnamon, honey, rose hips, saffron, marigold, rice, bay leaves, dandelion root, sunflower, walnuts and the palm tree.

Dandelion root stimulates the flow of gastric juices and saliva, and therefore assists in the digestive process. Rose hips are an excellent source of vitamin C, as are tomatoes, which are classified as a citrus fruit. Tomato juice is an anti-acid and clarifies the system. Honey is much better for you than white sugar.

Cinnamon tea, as a mild stimulant, serves to increase the functional actions of the system. Few people realize that tests have proved that cinnamon oil is a more powerful antiseptic than carbolic acid. In India, where there is intense heat and little refrigeration, it was found that cinnamon (among other spices) will preserve meat fats for quite a period of time.

Rice, especially unpolished, brown or wild rice, is one of

the most healthful food staples. It means subsistence to millions of people. Rice, being easily digested, is also recommended in the diet for heart patients. Saffron is used in rice dishes, sauces, cakes and fancy rolls, with chicken, fish, eggs, and is added to liquors, medicines and cosmetics. Saffron is very expensive, it takes the stigma of some 75,000 flowers to make one pound of saffron.

Many of the sun- (and Leo-) ruled herbs and spices have been used since ancient times as food, germicides, for medicinal purposes and in religious ceremonies. The Romans used marigold as a substitute for saffron and are credited with carrying the plant to England. Every possible use was made of it. It was said to cure skin diseases, warts, colds, jaundice, headache, toothache, bee stings, inflamed eyes, etc. Cooked marigold was used to stimulate a weak heart and was also used to color butter and in a rinse for the hair. Saint John's wort, also known as "Devil's Flight," a sun-ruled herb, was worn around the neck in Europe hundreds of years ago as a protective amulet and was hung in windows to frighten and chase away evil spirits.

From *Culpeper's Complete Herbal,* printed in the early seventeenth century, come these herbs and their uses:

Angelica: "So-named because of its angelical virtues . . . it resists poison by defending the heart, blood and spirits . . . openeth the stoppage of the spleen. . . . The juice droppeth in the eyes help dimness of sight . . . and the root in powder and laid on the biting of mad dogs or other venomous beasts, doth wonderfully help. . . ."

Bay: ". . . neither witch nor devil nor thunder nor lightning will hurt a place where a bay tree is . . . it resisteth witchcraft very potently. . . . The oil made of the berries is very comfortable in all cold griefs of the joints . . . it helpeth palsies, trembling, weariness also, and pains that come from back or belly."

Butterbur: "It is under the dominion of the Sun and therefore is a great strengthener of the heart and cheerer of the vital spirits. The decoction of the root, in wine, is singular good for those that wheeze much. It taketh away all spots and blemishes of the skin."

Burnet: "This is an herb of the Sun. . . . The continual use of it preserves the body in health and the spirit in vigor;

for if the Sun be the preserver of life under God, his herbs are the best in the world to do it. Two or three of the stalks with leaves put into a cup of wine, especially claret, are known to quicken the spirits, refresh and clear the heart, and drive away melancholy."

Centaury: "They are under the dominion of the Sun as appears in that their flowers open and shut as the sun showeth or hideth his face. . . . The juice of the herb with a little honey put to it is good to clear the eyes from dimness."

Poppy (yellow): "It is aperative and cleansing."

Saffron: "It quickens the brain, helps the difficulty of breathing, it is excellent in epidemical diseases. . . . It is said to be more cordial and exhilarating than any of the other aromatics. Saffron is endowed with great virtues, for it refreshes the spirits, it is good against the palpitation of the heart . . . and it is good to aid digestion."

Trefoil (heart): "It is a great strengthener of the heart and cherisher of the spirits, relieving those who faint and swoon. . . . It defends the heart against the noisome vapours of the spleen. . . ."

Vine tree: "The dried fruit comes from abroad under the names of raisins and currants . . . is the most gallant tree of the Sun, very sympathetical with the body; that is the reason why spirit of wine is the greatest cordial among vegetables."

Virgo

(August 22–September 22)

VIRGIN

THE ZODIACAL SYMBOL for Virgo is a corruption of the Greek word meaning "virgin." The sun passes through this sign when it is time for the harvest and the pictograph of Virgo shows a maid with a spike of grain in her hand.

Virgo is ruled by Mercury, as is Gemini, and both signs have some similar qualities and key words. Gemini, however, is an air sign whereas Virgo is an earth sign. Earth signs are apt to be more inhibited in self-expression than air signs, but if they free themselves of this limitation, they can be the most expressive of the triplicities.

As a Virgoan you are an idealist, and although your sign is not generally considered a creative sign, you often give materialization to your ideals through the creative arts, especially writing. Such famous writers as Theodore Dreiser, Dr. Samuel Johnson, Maurice Maeterlinck, Tolstoi and H. G. Wells were born with the sun in Virgo.

Earth signs enjoy material comforts, and you are no ex-

46

ception; however, Virgo is a sign of service and your true happiness often comes from helping others. Virgo rules the sixth house in the natural zodiac, which is the house of health and employment. You often combine these sixth-house matters with your desire to help mankind.

Margaret Sanger, the exponent of birth control, was such a Virgoan. She saw the plight of mothers, old and in ill health before their time from childbearing, and their hungry and sickly children, and she devoted her life to the unpopular and often condemned plan for alleviating such misery.

Employment, labor relations and unions go hand in hand in our modern society. Walter Reuther, a Virgo native, has struggled and fought to obtain better working conditions and higher wages for the automobile workers.

The Virgo native seeks perfection and is discriminating in his choice of a mate, attire or occupation. He is apt to be too exacting and critical and because perfection is hard to find, he becomes discontented. If you Virgoans will remember that "beauty is in the eye of the beholder," and use that introspective quality of yours, you may come to realize that the little faults you find in other people may be but a reflection of your own.

Some signs are content that a theorem or a mechanism works. You want to know why it works. You like to analyze, to dissect, to take something apart and put it back together. Many diagnosticians, watchmakers and repairmen were born in this sign.

You are methodical in your approach to any problems and extremely conscientious in whatever you do. Haphazard guesswork is alien to your nature. In your desire for perfection you have a tendency to repeat a procedure that is already satisfactory. That time and effort could be spent on something new. You have a fine mind, you are versatile and knowledgeable; it is up to you to make the most of your abilities. You can envision the scientific accomplishment or the better position, but you will have to terminate one endeavor before you can go on to the next. Do not be afraid of that next step.

You are courteous, well-mannered, and your natural bearing and demeanor will impress others. As a Virgoan you are honest, trustworthy, reliable, and you are not apt to shirk your share of responsibility. Together with these attributes, you have the ability to use your imagination for constructive and practical purposes, making you an asset to any organization.

Natives of your sign derive a great deal of enjoyment from reading, attending lectures or the theater. Intellectual pursuits stimulate your fertile brain. You have a retentive memory, and although you are not apt to display your knowledge, you can be an interesting conversationalist, especially when the subject matter is of a more serious nature than idle chit-chat.

With your superior powers of observation and keen perception, you make excellent proofreaders and literary critics. However, as you are subject to impulsive action, you must guard against letting any personal prejudices influence you. Take the time to analyze your judgment before you act. This would apply in any business or social contacts with others. Hasty or unjustifiable criticisms might cause heartache and estrangement.

Those of this sign are usually sensitive and reserved, and are not apt to show their real feelings, especially in affairs of the heart. The old saying that "opposites attract" does not often apply to Virgo natives. They are not as emotional as some signs and prefer someone with whom they have a mental as well as physical relationship. They have a tendency to accept marriage in a matter-of-fact way, unmindful that a show of affection and understanding will mitigate many of the differences that are apt to occur.

The Virgoan is more apt to find his niche in a profession wherein he can use his mental rather than physical abilities. Many of this sign have an aptitude for scientific research. Such work requires the accuracy, the deep concentration and the patience which are characteristic of Virgo. Virgo-born scientists include Ernest Rutherford, the first man to disintegrate the atom, Carl D. Anderson, who discovered the positron, and Michael Faraday, who discovered electromagnetic induction. Others have received world acclaim in the field of medical science. Walter Reed, a surgeon who discovered the connection between yellow fever and a certain kind of mosquito, was Virgo born.

Virgoans are usually practical, conservative and prudent. They consider the value of an item before they buy, preferring good quality and usefulness to the unnecessary or worthless. They may spend freely now and then, but they will have some financial reserve put aside for the rainy day. They are capable and industrious and their financial condition will be largely up to themselves.

The Virgo child is mentally quick, but as he does not have the drive of some signs, he may not use his intellect to its full capacity unless his interests are stimulated. Virgo children are fairly healthy, but are inclined to be picky in choosing food and may not eat well-balanced meals. They can be friendly, even though they have a tendency to be hypercritical. Outdoor exercise is essential as it acts as a tonic, both mentally and physically. Positive thinking in health matters by the parents of a Virgo child will do much to diminish his fears of illness.

The Virgo wife often runs her home like a business. She is capable, an excellent housekeeper; everything is in order, spotless and hygienically clean. She likes to buy her eggs from the farmer and her fish at the dock, to be sure they are fresh. In marital relations she may not be as passionate as those of other signs. Virgo is the sign of the Virgin and Virgo women are apt to remember that. She is best suited to a partner who is as practical and restrained as herself, unless, of course, other planetary influences alter her natural Virgo tendencies.

The Virgo man often prefers to remain a bachelor, but if he does marry, he would probably be happiest with a Virgo wife. He is conventional, very proper and not as predominantly male as some signs. He provides well for his family, but is apt to be a complainer about his health, expenses, or what have you.

Virgo and the sixth house are probably responsible for more health troubles than any other segment of the zodiac. This sign is closely associated with mental activity, and worry, tension, undue concern over health or any sustained mental strain will cause digestive upsets which, in turn, affects the entire system.

The Virgoan often goes from one physician to another or turns to faith healers, seeking advice and help for real or imaginary illnesses. A Virgo native often has many idiosyncrasies concerning food and is inclined to follow dietary fads. Some people, because of health problems, may be advised by their physician to eat only certain foods, but normally everyone needs a balanced diet, consisting of protein, carbohydrates, fats and the essential vitamins and minerals—and Virgo natives should keep this in mind.

Virgo rules the intestines, the alimentary canal, the abdominal cavity (and its membranes), the spleen, the lower lobe of liver and the duodenum.

The sign Virgo is susceptible to the following diseases: afflictions of the intestines and digestive tract, cholera, typhoid, peritonitis, malnutrition, tapeworm, appendicitis, intestinal paralysis, possibility of general paralysis in old age, and maladies obscure in origin. (Restricted diets often cause acidosis, which will be noted as muscle pain, fatigue and sore throat.)

As Virgoans are susceptible to afflictions of the intestines and digestive tract, as well as malnutrition, they, more than any other sign, should follow a dietary regimen that includes all the essentials. This means eating that variety of foods which supplies the body with all it needs, and in the proper amounts.

Nature, in creating foods for the human body, has balanced the elements in such a manner that man has a choice of foods that are both nourishing and palatable. Meat, fish and eggs are mostly protein and fats, whereas fruits and vegetables contain more carbohydrates. They all have a certain vitamin and mineral content. Virgoans should take particular note of the following:

ESSENTIAL VITAMINS*	SOURCES
Vitamin A: growth, anti-infective and eye vitamin; for cells of skin and mucous membrane	Fish-liver oils (especially halibut), whole milk, cheese, eggs, seafoods, salad greens, yellow vegetables, apricots
Vitamin B₁ (Thiamine): gland and nerve vitamin, for growth and to maintain normal appetite	Yeast, whole grains, legumes, eggs, lamb, okra, nuts, etc.
Vitamin B₂ (Riboflavin): for growth and nutrition	Lean meats, yeast, raw salads, milk, cheese, whole grains
Vitamin B₁₂: prevents pernicious anemia	Liver, milk, egg yolk, cheese, whole grains

* See last chapter for complete list.

ESSENTIAL VITAMINS*   SOURCES

Niacin: prevents pellagra, prevents digestive disturbances, helps the central nervous system

Wheat germ, parsley, fresh greens, most fruits

Vitamin C (Ascorbic acid): for teeth, gums, prevents scurvy, for small veins, stiff joints

All citrus fruits, tomatoes, raw cabbage, spinach, watercress, parsley, rose hips, watermelon, pimientos, etc.

Vitamin D: for bones, teeth, prevents rickets and nervousness

All fish-liver oils, seafoods, eggs, milk, onions, garlic, greens

Vitamin E: for fertility

Whole wheat, lettuce, shellfish, celery, raw sugar, cress

Vitamins K_1 and K_2: for blood clotting

Green-leaf vegetables, spinach, alfalfa

Vitamin P (Rutin): strengthens walls of veins, reduces swellings of tumorous nature

Paprika, lemon rind

ESSENTIAL MINERALS*   SOURCES

Calcium: builds bones, teeth

Nettles, watercress, chives, okra pods, arrowroot, cheese, lettuce, cabbage, poppy seed, lemons, etc.

Fluorine: for eyes, teeth, firm bones

Escarole, seafood, garlic, watercress, whole oats, corn, etc.

Iodine: for thyroid; to relieve nervous tension, prevents goiter, high blood pressure

Seafood, kelp, Irish moss, radishes, lettuce, squash, etc.

Iron: makes red blood, gives vitality, prevents anemia, mental fatigue, etc.

Sorrel, lettuce, romaine, parsley, strawberries, onions, spinach, rice bran, asparagus, liver, etc.

Magnesium: prevents constipation, insomnia, neurasthenia

Tomatoes, dill, lettuce, spinach, parsley, kale, cabbage, wintergreen, cucumbers, eggplant, etc.

Phosphorus: for bones, teeth, prevents neuritis, numbness, etc.

Kale, radishes, caraway seeds, garlic, sesame, licorice root, seafood, cheese, mushrooms, etc.

* See last chapter for complete list.

ESSENTIAL MINERALS*	SOURCES
Potassium: for body repair	Tomatoes, parsley, lettuce, celery, eggplant, stringbeans, turnips, etc.
Silicon: prevents nervous exhaustion, infection, mental fatigue, etc.	Lettuce, parsnips, asparagus, onion, horseradish, beets, cucumbers, etc.
Sodium: builds ligaments and tissues, helps saliva, bile and other juices, etc.	Celery, spinach, tomatoes, oysters, cheese, red beets, carrots, lettuce, leeks, pumpkin, asparagus, etc.
Sulphur: prevents infection, rids body of impurities	Watercress, garlic, okra, dill, Brussel sprouts, cabbage, etc.

* See last chapter for complete list.

Eat at regular times, when fully relaxed. When you are nervous or generally disturbed you suffer indigestion. If the food is not properly digested and assimilated all the value is lost. Forget the stomach pills, the digestive aids and the cathartics. Many herbs with a high vitamin and mineral content will also reduce the need for harmful drugs:

> *Calmatives*—take as a warm tea upon retiring: Catnip herb, camomile flowers, hops.
> *Nervines*—to relax temporarily from nervous strain or fatigue: Betony herb, nerve root, valerian root or yarrow herb.
> *Aromatics*—to expel gas from stomach or intestines: Fennel seed, ginger tea, angelica seed or peppermint herb.
> *Cathartic*—to increase the bulk of the feces and not irritate the delicate lining of the stomach: Psyllium seed.

There are many botanicals which are nutritive and easily digested. Arrowroot is an excellent carbohydrate and a good source of digestible calcium. Carob pods contain up to fifty percent natural sugar and are a good substitute for hard to digest pastries. Okra is highly recommended because of its vitamin and mineral content and as a demulcent. Sweet elm (or slippery elm) is easily digested and neutralizes stomach acids.

For a cooling beverage try borage herb, licorice root, pimpernel herb or raspberry fruit. There are numerous herb teas which have a delicate flavor and are nutritious as well:

Alfalfa tea: Alfalfa is one of nature's best sources of easily assimilated trace elements.

Rose hip tea: Contains vitamin C.

Sarsaparilla tea: An excellent alternative.

Spearmint tea: For nausea.

Summer Savory: To stimulate the functional action of the system. A more complete list of herb teas will be found in the last chapter.

Herbs have been used for thousands of years for flavoring, as food and as medicine. After careful and prolonged study, the astrologer-herbalists compiled their findings concerning the relationship between the planet or sign and various herbs. They considered what caused the disease, what part of the body was afflicted—whether flesh, blood, bones or ventricles— by what planet the afflicted part was governed, and what herb cured the disease. Old-time herbals listed hundreds of herbs and their functions. Many decoctions of herbs are used in modern medicine, but some of the uses listed in herbals of long ago may seem strange. This selection is from *Culpeper's Complete Herbal*, written in the early seventeenth century:

Bittersweet: "It is under the planet Mercury. It is good to remove witchcraft both in men and beast, and all sudden diseases whatsoever. Being tied about the neck, it is a remedy for the vertigo or dizziness of the head."

Calamint: "It is an herb of Mercury and a strong one too . . . the leaves boiled in wine, and drank, provoke sweat, and open obstructions of the spleen . . . it helpeth them that have any cold distemper in their bowels. Let not women be too busy with it, for it works very violently upon the feminine part."

Carrots: "Wild carrots belong to Mercury . . . is good for those whose bellies are swollen with wind."

Fennel (common): "The seed, and the roots much more, help to open obstructions of the liver, spleen and gall, and thereby ease painful and windy swellings. The roots are of most use in physic drinks and broths, that are taken to cleanse the blood . . . and to cause a good habit through the body."

Fenugreek: "It is under the influence of Mercury. The decoction, or broth of the seed, drank with a little vinegar, expels and purges all superfluous humours which cleave to the bowels."

Marjoram: "This is under the dominion of Mercury. It strengthens the stomach and head much; there is scarcely a better herb growing for relieving a sour stomach or loss of appetite; it cleanses the body of choler, expels poison, remedies the infirmities of the spleen, and helps the bites of venomous beasts. The whole plant is a warm aromatic, and an infusion of the dried leaves is extremely grateful."

Pomegranate tree: "This tree is under Mercury. Both the flowers and the bark are strongly astringent. The pulp of the fruit, when in perfection, is very grateful, and has the same general qualities with the other fruits."

Senna (red-flowered bladder): "It is under Mercury. The leaves are hot, dry and of a purging quality."

Libra

(September 23–October 22)

SCALES

THE SYMBOL OF Libra is that of the horizon, with half of the setting sun showing above it. The pictograph shows a pair of scales, significant of balance, justice and relationships.

Libra is the sign which begins at the westernmost point of the zodiac where the sun crosses the equator, and moves from the Northern to the Southern Hemisphere.

Libra belongs to the airy triplicity, which bestows a pleasing personality and which governs attachments. Librans, from the interpenetrative quality of air, seek mutual understanding and union between personalities and temperaments —in marriage, business and often in the diplomatic field.

The planet Saturn is exalted in Libra and challenges the sun in this sign. Librans, responding to the sun, are cheerful and optimistic, but when they react to the influence of Saturn, they become worried and melancholy.

Venus rules the sign Libra and bestows artistic ability upon those born at this time. Saturn adds constructive skill to the art of Venus; thus Librans often excel in the construc-

55

tive arts, such as jewelry design, decorating or architectural drafting.

Venus, a benefic planet, gives those of your sign a charm and graciousness unequaled by any other planet ruler. First impressions are always important, and you attract others easily, although you might be a little superficial in your attitude. You have an affable and persuasive manner which you can use to get what you want.

As a cardinal sign, you are ambitious, enthusiastic and usually quite practical; however, there are times when you are changeable and indecisive. It is often necessary to consider carefully an idea or a proposition before going ahead with it, and it is natural for you to weigh its respective merits, but you must be considerate if others are involved.

Libra (as a cardinal sign) bestows solidarity and cooperation in partnerships. You, better than any other sign, can achieve success in joint endeavors, especially if you are judicious and straightforward in your approach to any problems that may arise. Misleading or artful tactics will only complicate matters.

Your sign is associated with the arts, and many entertainers, musicians and writers have been Libra born. The long and noteworthy list 'includes George Gershwin, Giuseppe Verdi, Franz Liszt, Eleonora Duse, Helen Hayes and Eugene O'Neill. Other Librans, stimulated by their Venus influence, are florists, milliners, stylists, interior decorators, etc. Librans also have an extraprofessional interest in the artistic and beautiful—whether it be their personal wardrobe or general surroundings.

They are fastidious and quite conventional. Everything must be selected carefully with an eye for detail and proper fit. The same applies to the home. They are often propriety conscious and become overmeticulous in their desire for perfection. They want everything to be exactly right and are apt to be unduly anxious over some trifling matter. The harmony they desire might well become the apple of discord. The mate or partner could misunderstand these well-meant intentions and feel that such trivia should not be as important as mutual interests or responsibilities.

Very often the Libran will be confronted with two ideas or two propositions at the same time. He sees the advantage of each and would like to accept both. At times he will weigh and balance to the point of exasperating any others who may be involved; at other times his conclusions may stem from erroneous comparisons or poor judgment and he will act hastily.

The Libran is perceptive, considerate of others and has good sense. If he uses these qualities he will be able to reach the decision most advantageous to all concerned. He should guard against doing anything from a personal or prejudicial point of view; it is contrary to his nature, and if he does, he usually regrets it.

It is one of the attributes of Librans to be able to see both sides of a subject, whether in social conversation or heated debate. They prefer to mediate in such instances and thus they endear themselves to the opposing participants. If called upon to give a definite answer or to pass judgment upon a matter, they can be analytic and wise. They make excellent judges, jurists and diplomats.

Although Libra is not considered an emotional sign, these natives are inclined to be intelligent in any matter except their own feelings. Usually kind, generous and loyal, they are moody and rather touchy at times. Emotional balance is as important as mental balance, and the Libran would be wise to suppress any temperamental outbursts as they may have an adverse effect upon his health.

Libra-Venus give these natives a fondness for the good things of life, and they usually make a sincere effort to gratify their tastes and desires. Appropriate wearing apparel, a lovely home and furnishings are important, but, be he esthete or dilettante, he has a tendency to be fond of show and approval. His refined comportment, whether natural or acquired, gives the impression of being to the manner born, and his charm and tact dispel any hint of pretentiousness.

Those born under this sign lean toward the intellectual and artistic pursuits; they are proud and usually dislike menial tasks or positions. They can succeed in any capacity which may bring them before the general public. They are versatile and often experience difficulty in deciding just what they would like to do.

Librans have good earning power, but they have expensive tastes and are apt to be big spenders. They may be impulsive when they see something that appeals to them, but unless there are unlimited funds, these natives should apply their extraordinary sense of balance to their expenditures.

As noted earlier in this chapter, Libra is a partnership sign. These natives are particularly adept at handling any conditions or problems that may arise. A great deal, however, may depend upon the type of partner, or partners, involved. It would be wise to associate with those who are neither too sensitive nor too obstinate to give the same cooperation you are willing to give.

Libra children are fond of art, music, sculpture, etc., and their interest in anything of an artistic nature should be stimulated. Training for any particular aptitude should begin in the formative years while the child is not only more responsive to suggestions, but young Librans have a tendency to be changeable in their choice of a career. Libra children are generally good-looking with a lovely complexion, a graceful body and well-shaped hands and feet. They may be susceptible to headaches, kidney ailments or indigestion (often resulting from emotional upsets), but usually respond readily to treatment.

The Libra wife expresses the Venus influence in her attractiveness, charm and intelligence. She has a talent for harmony and cooperation in the home and among friends. She often leads an active social life, but never neglects her family obligations. She is amorous and responsive in marital relations, and even though she may be flirtatious and attract many admirers, she is not generally fickle. She is an interesting companion and a congenial partner.

Libra husbands are capable and they provide well for their families. They feel a need for the beautiful and luxurious in their home and surroundings. They are not as domestic as some signs and might be tempted to seek a little variety; however, they are conventional and will use all their persuasive and tactful attributes to solve any marital disagreements.

Each sign and each ruling planet has certain positive and negative characteristics. The higher-type individual will represent the positive qualities, but, if the ego is unable to control its emotions or passions, it will be more apt to reflect the negative qualities.

Some of the Libra-Venus positive and negative qualities

are: aesthetic or dilettante, original or imitative, ardent and zealous or lazy, temperate or profligate, modest or vain, well-mannered or boorish, artistic or gaudy and vulgar, constant or changeable, and judicious or imprudent.

In zodiacal anatomy, Libra rules the kidneys, ovaries, adrenals, loins, appendix, ureters, lumbar vertebrae and the skin in general. In zodiacal physiology Libra rules distillation, sublimation (chemical), filtration, glandular secretion, action of body liquids in general, and equilibrium of parts.

Libra-Venus disease tendencies include inflammation of kidneys, Bright's disease, all forms of kidney trouble, lumbago, diabetes, and weakness of the suprarenal gland.

Negative Libra-Venus influences, such as self-pity, depression, erotic tendencies, melancholia, ennui or temperamental outbursts, tend to age the Libra natives by depleting the nervous system. They are easily thrown off balance in health matters but respond to treatment.

Librans need to drink plenty of water and fruit juices, and limit their sugar intake because they are subject to kidney trouble. Social, romantic or marital strife can upset the Libran's health, and any severe emotional depression may induce escapism, often alcohol.

As the Libran has a tendency to be physically lazy, he should take up some form of exercise. Effective kidney action is necessary for a proper acid-alkaline balance. More fruit, salad, lean meat and less heavy food and pastries in the diet are suggested.

Venus rules peppermint, wheat, sweet-smelling spices, apples, pears, figs, apricots, gooseberries, grapes, almonds, and many healthful herbs. Libra rules copper and oxygen.

Proteins, carbohydrates and fats, and the various vitamins and minerals are necessary for building and maintaining a strong and healthy body. Below is a partial list of these essentials.

ESSENTIAL VITAMINS*	SOURCES
Vitamin A: for night vision, skin-cell function, mucous membranes, prevents infection	Butter, whole milk, cheese, liver, fish liver oils, green-leaf vegetables, yellow vegetables, fruits with yellow flesh

* See last chapter for complete list.

ESSENTIAL VITAMINS*	SOURCES
Vitamin B$_1$ (Thiamine): for growth; maintains normal appetite	Whole grains, yeast, legumes, lamb, eggs, nuts, brown rice
Vitamin B$_2$ (Riboflavin): strengthens veins; helps cure skin eruptions, bowel trouble, paralysis, etc.	Same sources as Vitamin A
Vitamin B$_{12}$: develops red blood cells for normal nutrition	Liver, egg yolk, alfalfa, kelp
Niacin: prevents pellagra, digestive disturbances; helps the central nervous system	Alfalfa leaves, parsley, wheat germ, watercress, etc.
Vitamin C (Ascorbic acid): for healthy teeth and gums; prevents scurvy; clears skin	Citrus fruits, tomatoes, tomato juice (either fresh or canned), raw cabbage, baked potato, red peppers, parsley, etc.
Vitamin D: for bones, teeth; prevents rickets	Seafood, fish-liver oils, eggs, butter, greens, onions, coconut oil, sardines, rose hips, parsley, oregano, etc.
Vitamin E: for fertility	Wheat germ or whole wheat, malt, alfalfa, shellfish, kelp, celery, fresh peas, raw sugar, etc.
Vitamin K: maintains normal clotting of blood and liver function	Green-leaf vegetables (especially spinach and alfalfa), cabbage, cauliflower and soybean oil
Vitamin P (Rutin): functions along with vitamin C	Paprika and lemon rind

ESSENTIAL MINERALS*	SOURCES
Calcium: for teeth and bones	Nettles, watercress, dill, chives, arrowroot, lettuce, dandelion root, okra pods, lettuce, milk, etc.
Fluorine: prevents skin diseases, anemia, curvature of spine; good for eyes, teeth, etc.	Whole oats, sea herbs and sea fish, cabbage, watercress, garlic, butter, beets, brown rice, etc.

* See last chapter for complete list.

ESSENTIAL MINERALS*   SOURCES

Iodine: for thyroid — Seafoods, kelp, radishes, milk, squash, asparagus, cabbage

Iron: repairs body; helps prevent anemia, physical and mental fatigue, etc. — Sorrel, lettuce, parsley, watercress, spinach, leeks, onions, strawberries, romaine, kale, etc.

Magnesium: helps prevent constipation, insomnia, neurasthenia. It is alkaline and laxative — Tomatoes, dill, spinach, kale, lettuce, cabbage, celery, sorrel, whole oats, cucumbers, corn, etc.

Phosphorus: vitalizes and repairs nervous system; prevents neuritis, paralysis, and softening of bones — Radishes, wheat bran, liver, caraway seeds, buttermilk, seafood, cheese, sesame, dill, etc.

Potassium: builds muscles for nerves; for body repair — Tomatoes, parsley, lettuce mushrooms, radishes, peppermint, romaine, string beans, parsnips

Silicon: helps prevent infection, nervous exhaustion — Lettuce, asparagus, horseradish, onions, rice bran, parsnips, etc.

Sodium: builds tissues; repairs body; gives strength and disease resistance; helps assimilate other chemicals; prevents arthritis, diabetes — Celery, tomatoes, romaine, cheese, some fish, oysters, carrots, chives, table salt, lettuce, etc.

Sulphur: stimulates system; prevents exhaustion, infection, jaundice, etc. — Garlic, watercress, kale, dill, raw cabbage, horseradish, chives, okra, sorrel, raspberries, etc.

* See last chapter for complete list.

A great many herbs have been used for thousands of years, some for medicinal purposes only and others in food—as a flavoring and to aid in maintaining health as well. Those listed especially for Libra include juniper berries for kidney disorders, camomile tea for weak stomach, celery seed for lumbago, dandelion root for liver complaints, sassafras bark tea for headaches caused by an acid condition and peppermint for gastric trouble.

Old-time herbals, and books on family medicine and home remedies were used extensively after the invention of the printing press, and although today the corner drugstore has

superseded these do-it-yourself prescriptions, most of the
medicines found in the modern pharmacy are decoctions containing many of these same herbs. Some of the former uses
for various herbs may seem strange to us. Consider this list
from *Culpeper's Complete Herbal*, printed in the early seventeenth century:

Alder: "It is a tree of Venus. The outward bark doth bind
the body and is helpful for all laxes and fluxes thereof . . .
it is singularly good to wash the teeth, to take away the pains
and to fasten those that are loose . . . the leaves are good
fodder for kine, to make them give more milk. . . ."

Archangel: "It makes the heart merry, drives away melancholy, quickens the spirits. . . . It is also very effectual to
heal green wounds and old ulcers. It draweth forth splinters
and such like things gotten into the flesh. . . ."

Cherries (winter): "This is a plant of Venus. . . . I shall
mention one way amongst others which might be used for
ordering the berries, to be helpful for the urine and the stone,
which is this: take three or four good handfuls of the berries,
either green or dried, and having bruised them, put them
into so many gallons of beer or ale when it is new and tunned
up: this drink taken daily hath been found to do much good
to many."

Chick peas: "They are under the dominion of Venus. They
are less windy than beans, but nourish more; they provoke
urine and are thought to increase sperm; they have a cleansing quality, whereby they break stone in the kidneys. The
white ones are so much more powerful than the garden kind
and are used more for meat than for medicine, yet have the
same effects, and are thought to increase the milk and seed."

Columbines: "It is also an herb of Venus. . . . The Spaniards used to eat a piece of the root thereof in the morning
fasting, many days together, to help them when troubled
with stone in the reins or kidneys."

Gooseberry bush: "They are under the dominion of Venus.
While they are unripe, being scalded or baked, they are good
to stir up a fainting or decayed appetite, especially where
the stomach is afflicted by choleric humours: they are excellent good to stay the longings of women with child."

Kidneywort: "Venus challenges the herb under Libra. It
helps sore kidneys, torn by the stone, or exulcerated within;
the juice heals kibes and chilblains. The distilled water, if

drunk, is good to cool inflammations and unnatural heats, a hot stomach, a hot liver or the bowels. . . ."

Peach tree: "Venus owns this tree. The leaves bruised and laid on the belly kill worms: and boiled in ale and rank, they open the belly . . . the fruit provokes lust. . . . If the kernels be bruised and boiled in vinegar until they become thick, and applied to the head, it marvelously makes the hair to grow again upon the bald places or where it is too thin."

Scorpio

(October 23–November 21)

EAGLE

THE ZODIACAL SIGN of Scorpio symbolizes the legs and tail (or, some say, just the tail) of the scorpion. The sign Scorpio symbolizes death, and as it governs procreation, it is also the symbol of generation and life.

On the mental plane this sign gives keen perception, intuition and resource of ideas. On the physical plane it represents the attributes of reproduction.

This sign is probably more complex than any other and is often assigned the eagle as well as the scorpion emblem. It can be materialistic or spiritual, or a combination of both. "The power of the spirit in the affairs of the world" is a key phrase for Scorpio.

Although the unevolved Scorpio native may express the characteristics of the scorpion—withdrawing into the dark, secret corners of his personality, suspicious and treacherous, ready to strike out with stinging sarcasm—it must be remembered that the scorpion rarely stings unless disturbed or provoked.

The highly evolved Scorpio responds to the qualities of the eagle. He is able to soar above the earthbound and purely physical plane of consciousness with courage, strength and self-control.

Scorpio is a fixed water sign. Generally speaking, fixed signs bestow tenacity, determination and deep powers of concentration.

Scorpio natives combine these fixed-sign qualities with an analytical, penetrating mind and an aptitude for scientific, philosophic or laboratory research and investigation. They are intuitive and imaginative, possessing a sensitivity to ideas and impressions, and the ability to visualize facts.

The new idea or concept intrigues the Scorpio. In his mind's eye he sees it as an actuality and is persistent in his efforts to make it so. He often gets a sudden inspiration of what to look for or what step to take next; consequently, he has the peculiar capabilities necessary for a chemist, a laboratory technician, a scientific researcher, a criminal investigator, etc.

All factors of an individual horoscope must be taken into consideration, as it should be evident that not all Scorpios would excel in such work. However, such outstanding natives of your sign as Marie Curie, discoverer of radium, and Dr. Jonas Salk, polio-vaccine researcher, should be an inspiration to all of you.

As with all signs, many talents and abilities are wasted because the native does not use them to their fullest extent. To you, as a Scorpio, if you get an idea, no matter how revolutionary it may seem, do not let it die a-borning; nurture it and let it grow. There is a great need for your particular abilities.

As a detective investigator, the Scorpio is shrewd and relentless. It has been said that the Scorpio detective, in seeking to correct past errors or to anticipate new moves or situations, plays a mental game of chess, with those involved being the chessmen. Whether or not this is true, he is usually quite successful.

Scorpios have the urge to uncover anything that is secret or hidden, to explore the unknown or to delve into the mysterious. Adm. Richard E. Byrd and Sir William Herschel (the astronomer who discovered the planet Uranus) were both Scorpio born. Scorpio archeologists dig into the earth searching for the remains of past civilizations, and Scorpio students of the occult search for the hidden truths of nature.

Mars, the co-ruler of Scorpio, rules all energy, whether constructive or destructive. Expressing their positive characteristics, Scorpios are forceful and courageous; they enjoy an occupation or enterprise that involves a certain amount of risk and that requires self-assurance and resolute action. They may be dynamic and high-spirited, displaying physical vigor and exuberance, such as President Theodore Roosevelt, or they may be the quiet, intellectual but equally determined type, such as Jawaharlal Nehru of India.

The Scorpio may or may not be a financial success, depending upon his attitude toward material wealth. There is an old saying that "Scorpios never die in the poorhouse." They have good earning ability, are resourceful and intuitive in financial matters. They are often better at handling other people's money than their own and, therefore, make shrewd and trustworthy bankers, financial advisers and insurance adjustors.

Although Scorpios enjoy the things that money can buy, they sometimes prefer to get away from the commercial skyscrapers and the pressures of our modern society to spend their time searching for the inner meaning of life.

All Scorpios benefit from a certain amount of quiet privacy now and then, to putter in a garden, to walk in the park or along the seashore. It may seem paradoxical that Scorpios, who have such an aptitude for probing the secrets of Nature, should find their *own* rehabilitation in silent communion *with* Nature.

Although artistry is not generally included in Scorpio-ruled occupations, many of this sign have become world-famous in acting (Sarah Bernhardt), art (Pablo Picasso), music (Ignace Paderewski), sculpture (Auguste Rodin) and literature (Robert Louis Stevenson).

Each sign (together with its ruling planet) has certain positive and negative characteristics, and if the native is aware of these tendencies, he may be more inclined to use the better qualities. The Scorpio-Mars native may be altruistic and magnanimous or he may be selfish and vindictive; he may be self-controlled and conciliatory or he may be quick tempered and quarrelsome; he may respect the rights of others or he may be domineering; he may be objective in his views or he may be opinionated and self-assertive.

Imperfections in character or disposition are problems to be overcome in learning the lessons of life. Your resourcefulness and indomitable will are strong factors in your endeavor to attain success. You should also strive to be more pliable and cooperative, as your own fixity of purpose might interfere with the views or rights of others. Scorpios have a charming, dynamic and magnetic personality when they express their more attractive qualities, but they only cause antagonism when they are sarcastic and self-satisfied.

Ordinarily you are generous, loyal and sympathetic, but you are also impulsive and you are apt to sever any relationship if you feel that the object of your affection or concern is taking advantage of you. You should try to understand the motives of others and not be hasty or vindictive in your reactions.

The Scorpio's ability to concentrate, oblivious to what is going on around him, enables him to think and meditate while in a crowded room or while performing his daily tasks. As a Scorpio you are observant and perceive the little details that may escape the notice of others, this helps you to interpret and remember the overall picture of a proposition or an experiment.

The Scorpio thrives on physical (and often mental) exertion, if he becomes ill he practically wills himself back to health. Inactivity bores and annoys him. He should, however, use common sense in all matters pertaining to health. If his occupation requires physical labor, he should spend some time reading, studying or in some hobby.

The sun in Scorpio gives a love for mysticism and often provides the native with some occult ability. As these individuals are prone to investigate the supernatural, philosophical study and meditation will not only gratify the spirit but will relax the body as well.

As Scorpio rules procreation and reproduction, the love nature of these natives is intense, passionate and somewhat aggressive. Love acts as an inspiration and stimulus, and if their love and desires are fulfilled, they present the more pleasing qualities of their personality.

If there are misunderstandings, or frustrations, they should make a sincere effort to avoid irrational and senseless jealousy or bitterness. You, as a Scorpio, should use your positive qualities, not only for your own advancement but for the appreciation and respect of others.

The Scorpio child will develop in temperament and self-control according to the way he is trained. It may take a firm hand and a will stronger than his own to mold him and bring out his better qualities, but he can be taught to be understanding and cooperative.

He is naturally secretive and should not be punished too severely if he confesses some misdemeanor. It would only tend to stress this practice.

Sex hygiene, and the reasons for physical and moral cleanliness should be explained at an early age, as he is susceptible to the implications of his sign, and has a very early interest in sex.

Ordinarily the vitality is quite strong. He needs a wholesome diet, with bland rather than highly spiced foods, fresh air and plenty of rest. Hot foods should be avoided. Encourage his talents and participation in group activities.

The Scorpio husband may be quite difficult to live with as he is apt to be possessive and tyrannical. His passionate nature seeks affection and continuous response to his desires, and even when fully gratified, he may be jealous and suspicious. He is competent and usually a good provider for his family.

The Scorpio wife loves her home and children, is capable and courageous, and if the husband is understanding of her natural desires and fulfills her physical and emotional needs, she is loyal and constant. However, if marital relations are not harmonious, she is apt to follow the dictates of her heart rather than her conscience. She is realistic in financial matters, and even though she prefers luxury, she can manage on a small income. She would be wise to learn to suppress her self-indulgent tendencies and to live the more spiritual side of her sign.

In zodiacal physiology, Scorpio rules procreation, reproduction, destruction and elimination, and controls pigmentation, especially red coloring in the blood. In zodiacal anatomy, Scorpio rules the generative organs, nasal bone, bladder, gall, pubic bone, lower lumbar vertebrae, prostate gland, colon, testicles and rectum.

Diseases to which these natives are subject include ruptures, hemorrhoids, fistulas, scurvy, diseases of the generative system in general, venereal disease, ulcers, toxic complaints, nasal catarrh, prostatic stricture and urethral stricture. Other susceptibilities, from the Mars influence, are inflammations and acute fevers, infections, operations, muscular and genital disorders, diseases of the blood, and contagious diseases in general. The Scorpio is also susceptible to accidents, anything involving machinery or sharp instruments.

The sun in Scorpio accentuates the intellectual and more temperate traits, whereas Mars, the ruler, brings out the sensual side of the sign. Thus, natives of Scorpio, responding to the sun, are moderate and often abstinent in their diet; those who are more disposed to the Mars influence have hearty appetites, prefer hot and spicy foods and stronger beverages. Adjust your diet according to your temperament and occupation; the energetic individual or one whose occupation requires physical labor can eat heartier food than one who sits at a desk or is of a more phlegmatic type.

Scorpio and the eighth house rule the lower digestive and eliminative systems, and this sign is probably the source of illness more than any other. The eliminative system must function properly or it can lead to auto-intoxication, creating other ills.

Scorpios should practice moderation in all things; emotional extremism is as detrimental to good health as physical intemperance. Those individuals with a choleric temperament usually suffer from acid indigestion; physical excesses lead to many ailments, and Scorpios especially should follow sensible dietary rules. Plenty of fruit, vegetables and whole wheat products are suggested. Chemical cathartics should never be used for constipation; the herb eliminants are much better. (Americans probably consume more digestive aids and "drugstore" eliminants than the rest of the world, and it would be a good idea if we changed our mode of living and many of our habits.)

The old saying, "An ounce of prevention is worth a pound of cure" applies to all signs, and correct diet is part of that ounce. The body requires proteins, carbohydrates and fats, plus the essential vitamins and minerals, for growth and body repair.

Most vegetables have multiple vitamins. Celery contains

vitamins A, B, C and E and calcium; okra contains vitamins A and B₁, calcium, sodium, and sulphur.

Herbs, which can be purchased at food markets or health-food shops or can be grown in your own garden, are excellent to supplement the diet or for medicinal purposes. Many such herbs contain essential vitamins and minerals and are also nature's remedy for disease.

Constipation is a Scorpio complaint, and herbs such as agar-agar, psyllium seed, blue-flag root and rhubarb root are

ESSENTIAL VITAMINS*	SOURCES
Vitamin A: for growth, night vision; an anti-infective; for cells of skin and mucous membrane	Butter, cream, cheese, dark green vegetables, eggs, seafoods, yellow vegetables, lean meat, etc.
Vitamin B₁ (Thiamine): for growth, glands, and nerves; helps maintain normal appetite	Yeast, whole grains, liver, kidneys, legumes, okra, kelp
Vitamin B₂ (Riboflavin): lack of this causes skin lesions, eye damage, bowel trouble, etc.	Whole grains, milk, cheese, eggs, green-leaf vegetables, lean meat, raw salads, some fruits
Vitamin B₁₂: helps develop red blood cells	Liver, meat, fish, grains
Niacin: aids digestion and nervous system	General diet containing meat, eggs, fresh milk, etc.
Vitamin C: for healthy teeth and gums; prevents scurvy	Citrus fruits, tomatoes, raw cabbage, bean sprouts, raw onions and red peppers, rose hips, parsley, oregano, etc.
Vitamin D: for bones, teeth; prevents rickets	Fish-liver oils, seafoods, egg yolk, butter, garlic, onions, greens, olive oil, cabbage
Vitamin E: for fertility	Wheat germ, lettuce, mushrooms, lamb, eggs, peas, sweet potatoes, molasses, peanuts, corn, etc.
Vitamins K₁ and K₂: for blood clotting	Green-leaf vegetables, especially alfalfa and spinach
Vitamin P (Rutin): an anti-hemorrhage vitamin	Paprika, lemon rind, etc.

* See last chapter for complete list.

ESSENTIAL MINERALS*

SOURCES

Calcium: for bones and teeth; for blood circulation, heart muscles
Arrowroot, watercress, cheese, milk, lettuce, raw cabbage, dandelion, okra pods, radishes

Fluorine: for teeth, eyes, bones, etc.
Escarole, cabbage, butter, corn, garlic, sea fish, brown rice, etc.

Iodine: for thyroid
Fish, especially sea fish, lettuce, asparagus, squash, etc.

Iron: prevents anemia, mental depression, etc.
Sorrel, lettuce, parsley, onions, radishes, spinach, strawberries, romaine, cabbage

Magnesium: is alkaline and laxative
Tomatoes, watercress, celery, dill, kale, whole oats, corn, figs, cauliflower, cucumbers

Phosphorus: an anti-acid; helps prevent softening of bones and teeth, neuritis, etc.
Bran, kale, caraway seed, seafood, buttermilk, cheese, liver, etc.

Potassium: for nerves, muscles, etc.
Tomatoes, lettuce, turnips, string beans, celery, parsley

Silicon: helps prevent mental fatigue, infection, etc.
Lettuce, onions, asparagus, rice bran, cucumbers, etc.

Sodium: an anti-acid; helps build and repair body
Celery, chives, carrots, cheese, tomatoes, okra, butter, beets

Sulphur: aid to elimination
Raw cabbage, kale, watercress, garlic, turnips, okra, etc.

* See last chapter for complete list.

mild and non-irritating. For inflamed generative organs try slippery elm or cramp bark; chickweed or mistletoe for hemorrhage (of lower organs), and sage or boneset for sore throat (Taurus, your opposing sign, rules the throat).

The practice of herb medication goes back through the centuries, and some of the old-time recommendations for their use may seem strange to us today. The seeds of sweet cicely, an excellent aromatic, were often crushed and used to polish floors. Samson snakeroot, an astringent, was carried as an amulet, in the belief it would make one strong.

Culpeper's Complete Herbal, printed in the early seventeenth century, contains a description of herbs with their medicinal properties. Some of the Mars-ruled herbs follow.

Basil (either garden or sweet): ". . . and away to Dr. Reason went I, who told me it was an herb of Mars, and under the Scorpion, and it is no marvel if it carry a kind of virulent quality with it. Being bitten by venomous beasts, it quickly draws the poison to it. It expelleth both birth and afterbirth; and as it helps the deficiency of Venus in one kind, so it spoils her actions in another."

Cuckoo-pint: "The leaves and roots, boiled in wine with a little oil added and applied to the piles or the falling down of the fundament, easeth them, and so doth sitting over the hot fumes thereof. The leaves either green or dry doth cleanse all manner of rotten or filthy ulcers, in what part of the body so ever. The powder taken with sheep's milk healeth the inward ulcers of the bowels."

Down, or Cotton thistle: "Mars owns this plant, and manifest to the world that though it may hurt your finger, it will help your body. Pliny writes that the leaves and root thereof, taken in drink, help those that have a crick in their neck. Galen saith they are of a healing quality and are good for such persons as have their bodies drawn together by some spasms or convulsion."

Nettle (common): "This is an herb of Mars. The seed being drunk, is a remedy against the bites of wild dogs. The juice of the leaves, or the decoction of the root, is good to wash fistulas, scabs or itches."

Onion: "Mars owns them. They are flatulent, or windy, and provoke appetite, increase thirst, ease the bowels, provoke the courses, help the bites of mad dogs, and of other venomous creatures, used with honey and rue; increase sperm, especially the seed. They kill worms in children . . . the juice is good for either scalds or burns. Used with vinegar, it takes away all blemishes, spots and marks in the skin. When plentifully eaten, they procure sleep, help digestion, remove obstructions of the viscera . . . bruised with a little salt and laid on fresh burns, draws out the fire and prevents them blistering."

Samphire (prickly): "This is a martial plant, and is more agreeable as a pickle than useful as a medicine. It is, however, strengthening to the stomach, procures an appetite, opens obstructions of the bowels and helps the jaundices."

Sagittarius

(November 22–December 21)

CENTAUR

THE SYMBOL OF Sagittarius is an arrow, with a short section of the bow, aiming at the stars. In the pictograph, the two legs of man, from the hips to the ankles, are condensed into one line, showing that, although the sign is dual in nature, there is a singleness of purpose.

Jupiter, the ruling planet of Sagittarius, signifies (among other things) breadth of vision. The Sagittarian benefits greatly from this planetary influence. The mind has an immense capacity for common sense and is open to reason; these attributes, combined with their humane and idealistic tendencies, are requisite qualities for statecraft. Many notable statesmen were born under this sign, including Benjamin Disraeli, Sir Winston Churchill, Charles de Gaulle, Josef Stalin, Robert G. Menzies, and Generalissimo Franco of Spain.

The Sagittarian is an electric philosopher, and once he believes in an idea or principle or forms an opinion, he wants to tell the world about it.

He is the promoter and the propagandist par excellence of

universal abstract ideas. If his sincerity and logic fail to convince his listeners, he will overwhelm them with his oratory.

Under ordinary circumstances he is diplomatic and tactful, and will try to overcome any opposition to his views or plans with the force of his sound and justifiable argument, but he tends to be impatient with those whose perception may not be as sensitive as his own. He can be amiable and impersonal, but he can also be quick-tempered and direct, and if the Sagittarian feels that his knowledge of a subject or his principles are being questioned, he may lose his usual self-control.

As a native of this sign, you are imaginative and progressive in thought and purpose. Your comprehension of the abstract serves to heighten your interest in law, religion and philosophy. Although you make a fine lawyer and an impartial judge, you are usually more interested in the science of law. You will probably study and compare dogmatics and metaphysics, and you may hold to one of the orthodox religions or you may incline toward ontology, for your sign indicates religious and philosophico-religious tendencies.

Sagittarius is a fire sign, with great driving power. You are observant, intellectual, penetrating in thought, and have the ability to concentrate on what interests you or what demands close mental application. These abilities can be used to further your success in whichever direction you may choose; however, you also have a tendency to be impatient and procrastinating, to put off the mental drudgery necessary to the full completion of any endeavor. Your inherent optimism is a great asset, but it will not do your work for you.

A spiritual or super-physical key word of Sagittarius is "the sea of the intuition." You may not be aware of this intuitive faculty, but it does give you prophetic insight into human nature and a cognition of facts.

Sagittarians are usually financially inclined, and although you are ambitious, you often get a later start toward a career or occupation than some other signs. This may be due to indecision on your part or to the fact that your independence means so much to you. You do not take kindly to suggestion or advice, and your "I'd rather do it myself" attitude is not in keeping with your basic charming personality. It would be to your advantage to be more amiable and less combative toward others.

The broad scope of your imagination, your energetic and venturesome traits enable you to consider seriously many and diverse occupations. You are well suited to the business world, especially large corporations or industries. You can visualize not only the beginning of an enterprise, but also its development and subsequent enlargement, as Jupiter, your ruling planet, signifies expansion. For example, Andrew Carnegie, the tycoon, started as a bobbin boy in a cotton mill and had the vision and daring that helped him build an industrial empire. Walt Disney, who sent little Mickey Mouse out into the world, by using his prodigious imagination and expansive tendencies has succeeded in bringing people from all over the world to Disneyland.

Sagittarius bestows altruistic, idealistic, intellectual, intuitive, philosophic and progressive characteristics upon its natives. Among prominent Sagittarians expressing these qualities we find: Spinoza, philosopher; Pope John XXIII, religious leader; Thomas Carlyle, Noel Coward, Mark Twain and Rudyard Kipling, authors; Diego Rivera, artist; Jan Sibelius and Ludwig van Beethoven, composers; John Milton, poet; and José Iturbi, pianist.

Rarely do we find Sagittarians who are at a loss for words. They are penetrating in thought and forceful in speech. When they so desire, they can be jovial and witty, but they can also be blunt and obstinate.

The Sagittarian who is open to reason and who will consider another's viewpoint or proposition stands a much better chance of self-improvement and success than the one who is too imbued with his own way of thinking or who deems it a matter of personal pride to display his independent nature. One can achieve true independence only by being cooperative with others, as all illustrious Sagittarians so ably demonstrate.

You have an almost obsessive desire to help other people. You are kind, benevolent and just, and although you may give others the benefit of your experience, you are not apt to be importunate. You firmly believe "Thou shalt not impose" and "Thou wilt not be imposed upon."

The symbol of Sagittarius shows that there are two widely different inclinations possible in these natives. The one inspires them toward higher learning, honorable conduct and morality. They become philosophers, pillars of the church, judges, physicians and reputable individuals in any occupation. The other impels them toward restlessness, get-rich schemes and speculative adventures, and they often become compulsive gamblers, racetrack habitués or soldiers of fortune, afflicted with too "lusty livers."

Although the Sagittarian possesses financial ability, he is not always conservative in money matters. If he uses his inherent good judgment in business ventures and limits his impulsive spending, he should attain a reasonable amount of financial security.

Sagittarius is a travel sign and you enjoy movement. Many of this sign participate in sports, either as a profession or for recreation; some of you like to dance and most of you like to walk. The Sagittarian often suffers from mental or physical claustrophobia and travel is excellent therapy. In fact, you are the most peripatetic of all the signs, and can even think better while moving about in a room or walking outdoors. It was a Sagittarian, Thomas Cook, who founded the famed travel agency, probably to facilitate matters for others like himself. You can be most successful far from your place of birth.

Sagittarius children are ambitious, curious and utterly frank. They are often temperamental and unpredictable and should be taught the principles of good behavior. It would be wise to nip in the bud any extravagant or wagering tendencies. They need exercise, plenty of fresh air and a rather strict diet.

The Sagittarius wife is intelligent, is interested in civic and social affairs and is an enthusiastic companion in sports activities. She is competent in home management and patient with her children. In marital relations she is excitable and highly responsive. She could be a good conversationalist as she is clever and usually well informed, but she is apt to be tactless, undiplomatic and self-assertive.

Ordinarily, the chief concerns of the Sagittarius husband are his business obligations, world affairs or sports activities. Too much domesticity dispels his interest and it takes a wise and understanding wife to hold him. His fluctuating emotions often cause misunderstandings and his desire for independence may lead to divorce.

Each sign, together with its ruling planet, governs certain areas of the body; they control the physiological functions and show tendencies which might develop into infirmities. In zodiacal anatomy Sagittarius rules the hips, thighs, coccygeal vertebrae, sacral region, sciatic nerves, and Jupiter rules the viscera, liver, arterial system suprarenals, fibrin of the blood, glycogen, right ear, upper forehead and, especially, the thighs and hips. According to zodiacal physiology, Sagittarius rules the motor nerve action, extension of sensory faculties, motion of organs and parts, and Jupiter rules molecular nutrition, cell development, building of blood, sustaining power and flesh building.

Diseases or infirmities to which these natives are susceptible include rheumatism, coxalgia, dislocation of hip joints, gout, sciatica, locomotor ataxia, blood disorders, liver trouble, pleurisy, dental trouble, fatty degeneration, diabetes, apoplexy, high blood pressure and heart trouble. These natives are especially venturesome and often accident prone, and their restlessness causes nervous depletion. They have strong appetites, but with sufficient exercise and proper diet, they need not suffer from overweight and its consequent disabilities.

Those of your sign in sedentary occupations or otherwise confining employment should get as much physical exercise as possible, especially in the open air. Exercise does stimulate the appetite; a serving of celery, raw carrots, radishes, etc., or a vegetable juice cocktail before lunch and dinner will abate the hunger and also provide essential nutriments.

Sagittarians generally have a strong constitution, and with a small amount of effort and common sense on your part, you can keep it that way. Proper balance, embracing both the mental temperament and the physical body, is needed to maintain good health. Negative thinking, nervous anxiety, short temper, improper diet and lack of sufficient exercise and rest will upset this balance.

You have a tendency to put on weight, especially if a woman Sagittarian, around the hips and thighs, and although your natural buoyancy may help to counteract this proneness, you should use moderation in food and drink consumption. Rich pastries, a meat and potato diet, and alcoholic beverages will put weight on rapidly. Raw salads, vegetables, fish, lean meats and fruit will fill you *up*, but not *out*. Study the following list of foods and choose a diet that will provide you the essential food elements without adding weight.

ESSENTIAL VITAMINS*	SOURCES
Vitamin A: for night vision, growth, skin and mucous membrane; an anti-infective	Butter, cream, cheese, fish-liver oils, dark green-leaf vegetables, carrots, fruits with yellow flesh
Vitamin B₁ (Thiamine): gland (thyroid) and nerve vitamin for growth and repair	Whole-grain products, yeast, eggs, lamb, legumes, liver, kidney, nuts, brown rice, avocado, asparagus, etc.
Vitamin B₂ (Riboflavin): lack of this vitamin causes skin lesions, eye damage, bowel trouble, hardening of the arteries	Whole grains, egg yolk, cheese, raw salads, milk, lean meats, most fruits, etc.
Vitamin B₁₂: prevents pernicious anemia	Liver
Niacin: prevents disturbances of digestive system and central nervous system; helps prevent pellagra	Liver, whole grains, all greens, milk, cheese, eggs, most fruit
Vitamin C (Ascorbic acid): for teeth, gums, prevents scurvy; helps clear the skin	Citrus fruits, tomatoes, baked potato, raw cabbage, peppers, onions, bean sprouts, turnip, greens, watermelon, strawberries
Vitamin D: for bones, teeth; prevents rickets, lack helps to cause nervousness	Seafoods, fish-liver oils, milk, cheese, butter, onions, garlic, greens, olive oil, chicken liver, etc.
Vitamin E: for fertility	All whole grains, lettuce, celery, fish, corn, peas, legumes, eggs, etc.
Vitamin G and K: necessary in process of blood clotting	Legumes, wheat germ, watercress, alfalfa leaves, etc.
Vitamin P (Rutin): strengthens tiny blood vessels	Paprika, lemon rind, buckwheat

ESSENTIAL MINERALS*	SOURCES
Calcium: for bones, teeth; strengthens heart muscles, arteries	Soup bones, watercress, cheese, kale, nettles, lettuce, cabbage, okra, milk, celery, lemons, onions, etc.
Fluorine: for teeth, bones, eyes	Sea fish, escarole, cabbage, garlic, bran, eggs, brown rice, etc.

* See last chapter for complete list.

ESSENTIAL MINERALS*   SOURCES

Iodine (thyroid chemical): helps prevent goiter, high blood pressure, nervous tension — Seafood, fish, lettuce, radishes, cabbage, asparagus, etc.

Iron: helps make red blood; prevents anemia, mental fatigue, miscarriage, etc. — Sorrel, lettuce, spinach, romaine, radishes, strawberries, cucumbers, liver, mushrooms, asparagus, etc.

Magnesium: aids assimilation of vegetables; prevents constipation; a gland and sex chemical — Tomatoes, lettuce, cabbage, spinach, dill, kale, okra, whole oats, etc.

Phosphorus: repairs and helps the nervous system; keeps acids out of blood, etc. — Cheese, mushrooms, watercress, kale, radishes, seafood, liver, lean meat, bran, cauliflower, turnips

Potassium: builds muscles; is alkaline and laxative; helps build and repair body — Tomatoes, lettuce, celery, turnips, kale, eggplant, parsnips, string beans, parsley, etc.

Silicon: helps prevent nervous exhaustion, mental fatigue, and infection — Lettuce, asparagus, rice bran, onions, spinach, cucumbers, etc.

Sodium: helps build tissues and ligaments; aids in dissolving other chemicals; gives resistance and endurance — Celery, raw salads, oysters, red beets, tomatoes, cheese, okra, carrots, chives, butter, etc.

Sulphur: helps enliven the whole system — Kale, watercress, mushrooms, nuts, Brussels sprouts, raw cabbage, etc.

* See last chapter for complete list.

Herbs for medicinal purposes have been used for countless centuries, and many of these same herbs are still being used in modern medicine. Some of the old-time "virtues and properties," however, may seem strange. For example, from *Culpeper's Complete Herbal,* published in the early seventeenth century.

Argrimony: "It is an herb under Jupiter and strengthens those parts under this planet and removes diseases in them by sympathy; and those under Mars, Saturn or Mercury, by antipathy, if they happen in any part of the body governed by Jupiter, and therefore must be good for the gout. It openeth and cleanseth the liver . . . healing all inward wounds, bruises and hurts. The decoction of the herb made with wine, and drank, is good against the biting and stinging of serpents. The leaves and seeds, being stamped with old swine's grease, helpeth old sores and draweth forth splinters, thorns, etc."

Asparagus: "It is under the dominion of Jupiter. The young buds or branches boiled in ordinary broth, make the belly soluble and open; and boiled in white wine or vinegar, it is prevalent for them that have their arteries loosened, or are troubled with the hip gout or sciatica. The decoction of the roots boiled in wine and being taken fasting several mornings together, stirreth up bodily lust in man or woman, whatever some have written to the contrary."

Betony (wood): "The herb is appropriated to the planet Jupiter. A Musa physician to the Emperor Augustus Caesar, wrote a peculiar book of the virtues of this herb; and among other virtues saith of it that it preserveth the liver and body of man from the dangers of epidemical diseases, and from witchcraft also. It killeth the worms in the stomach, openeth obstructions both of the liver and spleen. It is commended against the biting of serpents or mad dogs. A dram of the powder, taken with a little honey in some vinegar, doth refresh those that are wearied by travel. These are some of the virtues Musa, an expert physician, for it was not the practice of Octavius Caesar to keep fools about him, appropriates to betony."

Fig tree: "The tree is under the dominion of Jupiter. The milk that issues out from the leaves or branches where they are broken off, being dropped upon warts, takes them away. The decoction of the leaves is excellent good to wash foreheads with; a syrup of the leaves being drunk inwardly, dissolves congealed blood caused by bruises or falls. The juice being put into a hollow tooth eases the pain; as also deafness and pain in the ears, being dropped into them. A syrup made of the leaves or green fruit is excellent for coughs or hoarseness; it is very good for the dropsy."

Sage (common garden): "Jupiter claims this; and it is good for the liver and to breed blood. . . . It also helps the memory, warming and quickening the senses . . . boiled with other herbs it warms cold joints."

Capricorn

(December 22–January 20)

GOAT

CAPRICORN, THE TENTH sign of the zodiac, has for its symbol a pictograph bearing a resemblance to the horns of a mountain goat and the human knee.

It is a cardinal-earth sign ruled by the planet Saturn. Generally, cardinal signs bestow ambition, pride, enthusiasm and practicality. Capricorn itself bestows perseverance, tremendous will power and political, scholarly and/or material ambition. As an earth sign it denotes outward environment, social standing, recuperative power and resourcefulness.

Capricorn governs the professional and public life, and the esteem in which the native is held. A native of this sign will employ all his talents to reach the top in whichever occupation he chooses or in which circumstances place him. He is acutely aware of public opinion and instinctively knows what will impress and please the populace.

A Capricorn is extremely proud of his self-sufficiency; he does not seek help in the usual sense of the word, but he is adept at taking advantage of a situation or a person of higher business, social or political standing. His tactics are usually

81

open and above board, as his good name and the respect of others is as important to him as his personal success.

Saturn, the ruling planet of Capricorn, is known as the "celestial taskmaster," and natives of this sign often meet with delays, obstacles and restrictions in their efforts to get ahead. However, Saturn bestows the impetus, the persistence and the laboriousness necessary to the pursuit of ambitions or plans. A Capricorn almost always has to work hard to get started and really earns what he finally achieves.

The Capricorn is conscientious in whatever he does, and being exacting in his own procedure he expects it from his associates or partners. He demands facts and efficiency, and is exasperated by ineffective action.

These natives take their obligations seriously, whether to their employer or to anyone who has done them a favor. They are appreciative of any support or act of kindness and will be sure to reciprocate.

Because of their serious nature, Capricorns may appear timid and inhibited. If they let these feelings turn inward they indulge in self-pity and become cold and irritable. However, once they have overcome these tendencies, they are charming, dynamic and expressive. Their natural reserve will not permit them to be over-demonstrative, especially in public, but they can be warm, sympathetic and quite sensitive.

Although your sign denotes tact, caution and patience, you are apt to be impulsive and self-assertive when your feelings are aroused. Many of your sign have prejudices or preconceived ideas on matters, and it would be well if you would be more diplomatic and reasonable, and think before you speak.

Ordinarily you do not argue just to be disagreeable; you want to know what others think about a subject. But much unhappiness could be avoided if you would analyze their views and judge them fairly before you discredit them. It is often good policy to adjust your personal feelings to the situation and to examine your own views on a subject.

Saturn is the planet of crystallization. Unbending attitudes or fixed opinions can limit your advantages. As a Capricorn you are perceptive and somewhat intuitive, qualities which should help you understand human nature and motives. Awareness of one's own negative characteristics can be the first step toward improvement.

Factors other than just the sun and ruling planet must

always be considered before a particular talent or ability can be determined. However, Capricorns have become successful in practically every profession or occupation. This sign bestows tremendous will power, good financial and business acumen and a great capacity for detail. Politicians, actors, specialists, professors and many conservative lines of business come under this sign. It is an earth sign and miners, farmers, real-estate dealers also come under Capricorn. Many Capricorns are proficient and capable in more than one field. Woodrow Wilson, a college professor, became our twenty-eighth President, Benjamin Franklin was a printer, diplomat and scientist. Howard Hughes combines aviation and the motion-picture industry.

A long and impressive list of famous Capricorns includes Carrie Chapman Catt, woman's suffrage leader; Jean François Champollion, founder of Egyptology; Admiral George Dewey; Louis Pasteur, chemist; Sir Isaac Newton, astronomer; John Singer Sargent, painter; Sir Henry Bessemer, inventor; Daniel Webster, statesman; Pierre Samuel DuPont, industrialist; Andrew Johnson and Millard Fillmore, American Presidents; Henri Matisse, artist; Carl Sandburg, poet and biographer; J. Edgar Hoover, F.B.I. administrator; Danny Kaye, comedian; and Albert Schweitzer, physician and philosopher.

As a Capricorn you are thrifty, conservative and economical, and if you are thought to be materialistic, it is because of your desire for financial security. You are down-to-earth people, and first you consider the foundation, whether it be your home, business or profession. There may be times when opportunity comes unexpectedly or circumstances demand that you take what is available, but if possible, you prefer to plan your life, and you are systematic in your approach to every phase of it.

In preparing for a profession you are diligent and studious, acquiring as much knowledge as possible; in business you like to build from the ground up. You are dependable, responsible and you acquaint yourself with the details of situations you may be involved in. You are quite domestic, and home and family are important to you. You like to organize your home and you place a great deal of emphasis on loyalty and togetherness.

Each ruling planet represents certain positive and negative

characteristics. The higher or more evolved individual will generally express the positive qualities, whereas the unevolved type reflects the negative trends. Self-discipline, meditation and spiritual development will assist the consciousness in controlling any ignoble or unsympathetic tendencies. Those persons influenced by Saturn may be faithful, analytical, systematic, tactful, thrifty, cautious, responsible, punctual, chaste, studious, and just. They may also be avaricious, debased, fatalistic, jealous, pessimistic, stern, secretive and suspicious.

Many Capricorns are worriers—about their business, their health, what will happen tomorrow, next year or in ten years. Those so inclined should direct their will power toward a more rational and confident attitude.

Capricorn children, although often timid in the presence of strangers, are born leaders and organizers. They are dignified and well mannered, and usually prefer a few good friends to large so-called social groups. These children, if encouraged and trained, could reach the heights in many occupations. They resent restrictions and admonitions, and it takes tact and patience on the part of the parents to discipline them and still retain their trust and cooperation. The health of the Capricorn child should be watched carefully because the vitality is apt to be low; as they grow older the sun gives them resistance. Next to Scorpio, Capricorns have a longer life expectancy than any other sign.

The Capricorn wife is apt to be reserved and it is difficult for her to express her tender and affectionate feelings. Although she may not be as coquettish as some signs, she is capable of true and lasting love. She is ambitious for the success of her husband and concerned about the welfare of her children. She may economize on some things and then spend it on wearing apparel or a social affair.

The Capricorn husband, although usually successful financially and a good provider, is apt to be arrogant and domineering. He is the master, and determines the expenditures and the family routine. His passions are strong and he is generally a good marital companion to his wife.

In zodiacal anatomy Capricorn rules the knees, kneecaps, hair, outer epidermis, various joints of the body and bones in general. Diseases or infirmities to which the Capricorn is most susceptible are skin diseases, articular rheumatism, gout, hysteria, leprosy, infantile paralysis, deformities of the skeleton, erysipelas, dislocation of bones, splintered and broken bones, toothaches, inflammation of synovial membrane and stiffness of joints caused by bony tissue in joint space.

Saturn rules the skin, skeleton, hearing, gall bladder, teeth, ligaments, movable joints, vagus nerve, knees, the part of the intestine between the colon and the rectum, the left ear and the secretive system. Saturn-ruled diseases or infirmities include chronic diseases, paralysis, deafness, skin diseases, dry consumption, gangrene, atrophy, spinal ailments, impeded circulation, hardening of arteries, gout and rheumatism.

Many functional and organic disorders are caused by pathological factors which, in Saturn-ruled Capricorn, may be fears, inhibitions, pessimism or fatalistic inclinations. If you, as a Capricorn, are letting such factors impair your health you should use your tremendous will power to dispel these negative tendencies.

Saturn is cold, dry, restricting and limits the circulation; therefore, Capricorns generally should select a diet carefully. The astrological diet is very simple, yet it can go far toward maintaining good health. If you are in the habit of eating the same foods day after day, you should try to vary your diet by including a variety of vegetables and some of the herbs that add flavor as well as essential vitamins and minerals. As you have a tendency to a cold stomach, you should avoid iced drinks before and during meals. Study the food list below and choose a diet that will provide you with the essentials.

ESSENTIAL VITAMINS*

Vitamin A: a growth and anti-infective vitamin; for night vision, cells of skin and mucous membrane

Vitamin B₁ (Thiamine): gland and nerve vitamin for growth and repair

Vitamin B₂ (Riboflavin): pre-

SOURCES

Halibut, fish oil, butter, milk, cheese, eggs, dark green-leaf vegetables, escarole, parsley, yellow vegetables, etc.

Whole grains, yeast, eggs, legumes, kelp, okra, liver, etc.

Liver, kidneys, lean meats,

* See last chapter for complete list; also list of proteins, carbohydrates, and fats.

ESSENTIAL VITAMINS*	SOURCES
vents skin lesions, eye damage, bowel trouble, paralysis, etc.	milk, turnip and beet tops, egg yolk, broccoli, etc.
Vitamin B_{12}: develops red blood cells; prevents anemia	Liver, lean meat, fish, whole grains
Niacin: prevents pellagra; helps digestion and nervous system	Eggs, meat, fish, wheat germ, alfalfa leaves, etc.
Vitamin C (Ascorbic acid): for healthy teeth, gums; aids bone injuries, etc.	Citrus fruits, tomatoes, raw cabbage, baked potato, onions, rose hips, oregano, etc.
Vitamin D (the sunshine vitamin): for bones, teeth; prevents rickets	Fish, liver oils, eggs, milk, etc.
Vitamin E: for fertility	Whole wheat and wheat germ, lettuce, watercress, celery, lean meat, raw sugar, eggs
Vitamins K_1 and K_2: necessary for blood clotting	Grains, legumes, fresh vegetables
Vitamin P (Rutin): to strengthen tiny blood vessels	Buckwheat, lemon rind, paprika

ESSENTIAL MINERALS*	SOURCES
Calcium: for bones, teeth; maintains healthy arteries; prevents rheumatic tendencies, rickets, etc.	Cheese, milk, nettles, cabbage, arrowroot, okra, kale, lettuce, watercress, etc.
Fluorine: helps prevent anemia, skin diseases, curvature of spine, etc.	Sea herbs and sea fish, escarole, garlic, whole oats, butter, etc.
Iodine: for thyroid; prevents goiter, erratic tendencies, etc.	Fish seafoods, shellfish, kelp, radishes, asparagus, etc.
Iron: for blood; prevents anemia, depressions, mental fatigue, tuberculosis, etc.	Fresh bones (soup), lettuce, parsley, Swiss chard, romaine, strawberries, watermelon, kale
Magnesium: alkaline and laxative; prevents constipation, neurasthenia, etc.	Tomatoes, dill, cabbage, dandelion, celery, rice bran, cauliflower, etc.

* See last chapter for complete list; also list of proteins, carbohydrates, and fats.

ESSENTIAL MINERALS*   SOURCES

Phosphorus: helps prevent nervous disorders, softening of teeth and bones, numbness, etc.

Wheat bran, liver, seafood, cheese, watercress, radishes, spinach, cucumbers, dill, etc.

Potassium: builds and repairs muscles; for nerves; and helps prevent hardening of arteries

Tomatoes, parsley, lettuce, kale, sorrel, mushrooms, parsnips, peppermint, eggplant, etc.

Silicon helps prevent nervous exhaustion, infection, mental fatigue, etc.

Lettuce, asparagus, parsnips, rice bran, radishes, onions, etc.

Sodium: builds solid tissues, ligaments; helps prevent arthritis, gall and bladder stones; helps give a healthy color to skin

Celery, carrots, cheese, oysters, pumpkin, red beets, tomatoes, butter, okra, radishes, etc.

Sulphur: helps rid body of impurities; stirs up bile; enlivens the system

Kale, watercress, garlic, dill, horseradish, mushrooms, cabbage (raw), Brussels sprouts, okra, etc.

* See last chapter for complete list; also list of proteins, carbohydrates, and fats.

Most vegetables contain multiple vitamins and minerals. Such herbs as dill, caraway seed, celery tops, lamb's lettuce, fennel, sarsaparilla and hops may prove beneficial to those born under Capricorn.

Herbs have been used for countless centuries as food and for medicinal purposes. The ancients passed their knowledge on by word of mouth until the invention of the printing press. The astrologer-herbalists then printed them in book form. Some of the "virtues" ascribed to various herbs may seem strange to us of today, who think in terms of pills, shots, antibiotics, etc. From *Culpeper's Complete Herbal,* printed in the early seventeenth century, the following descriptions:

"By the icon or image of every herb, the ancients first found out their virtues. Modern writers laugh at them for it; but I wonder in my heart how the virtue of herbs first became known, if not by their signatures; the moderns have them from the writings of the ancients; the ancients had no writings to have them from: but to proceed." [Please note

that these "modern writers" he speaks about were his con-
temporaries.]

Amaranthus: "It is under the dominion of Saturn and is
an excellent qualifier of the unruly actions and passions of
Venus, though Mars should also join with her. The flowers
stops all fluxes of blood, bleeding either at the nose or wound
. . . and is a most gallant anti-venereal and a singular remedy
for the French pox."

Barley: "It is a notable plant of Saturn; if you view dili-
gently its effects by sympathy and antipathy, you may easily
perceive a reason for them; as also why barley-bread is so
unwholesome for melancholy people. Barley is more cooling
than wheat, and a little cleansing, and such things as barley
water or poultices do help much. A plaster made of barley-
meal with honey and oil of lilies and applied warm, cureth
swellings under the ears, throat, neck and such like."

Blue-bottle: "As they are naturally cold, dry and binding,
so they are under the dominion of Saturn. The powder or
dried leaves is given with good success to those that are
bruised by a fall or have a broken vein; being taken in the
water of plantain it is a remedy against the poison of the
scorpion, and resisteth all venoms and poison."

Dodder of thyme: "All dodders are under Saturn. He is a
physician indeed that hath wit enough to choose his dodder,
according to the nature of the disease and humour peccant
. . . for it draws nourishment from where its roots are, and
thus you see old Saturn is wise enough to have two strings
to his bow. This is accounted the most effectual for melancholic diseases . . . it openeth obstructions of the gall,
whereby it profiteth them that have the jaundice. Sympathy
and antipathy are two hinges upon which the whole model
of physic turns; and that physician who minds them not, is
like a door off from the hooks, more like to do a man mis-
chief than to cure him."

Mullein (white): "It is under the dominion of Saturn . . .
three ounces of the distilled water of the flowers drank morning and evening is a remedy for the gout. The seed bruised
and boiled in wine, and laid on any member that has been
out of joint, and newly set again, takes away all swelling and
pain."

Quince tree: "Saturn owns this tree. The crude juice is

preservative against the force of poison. The cotton or down boiled, and applied to plague sores, heals them up; and laid as a plaster, made up with wax, it brings hair to those that are bald, and keeps it from falling off, if it be ready to shed."

Ivy tree: "It is under the dominion of Saturn. A pugil of the flowers, about a dram, drank twice a day in the wine, helps the lax and bloody-flux. It is an enemy to the nerves and sinews, being much taken inwardly, but very helpful to them being outwardly applied. The fresh leaves boiled in wine will cleanse old ulcers, if washed with it. It also quickly heals green wounds, and is effectual to cure all burns and scalds; the juice of the berries or leaves, snuffed up the nose, purges the head and brain of thin rheum; the same dropped into the ears, helps the old and running sores in them."

Solomon's seal: "Saturn owns the plant. The root is available for wounds, hurts and outward sores. It dispels congealed blood that comes of blows, bruises and also takes away the black and blue spots that come from the same cause. It takes away freckles from any part of the body."

Aquarius

(January 21–February 19)

WATER BEARER

THE PICTOGRAPH OF Aquarius shows two parallel wavy lines. These signify both waves of water, and the masculine and feminine vibrations of electricity. The advance in the progress of civilization is manifested in this sign, as it represents the crest and the trough of waves. All progress is a matter of high points and low points, the push forward, the step backwards, and the forward advance again.

Aquarius is a fixed air sign, and as a native of a fixed sign, you are persistent, analytical and concentrative. Your perceptive powers are extremely acute; you can recognize and understand the nature of an idea or the motives of an individual. You are not likely to accept any new theory until you have studied, examined and classified it, but after you have become convinced of its merit you are inflexible in your defense and support.

Air signs in general denote the intellectual temperament

and relationships. As an air sign you express your intellect by your interest in literature, science, philosophy, the arts—any and all mentally stimulating branches of learning. The air sign Gemini rules the relationship with brothers and sisters, Libra with partners, and Aquarius with friends and with humanity in general.

Aquarius is ruled by Uranus, the planet of originality, inventiveness, spontaneity and the new order. Thus, the Aquarian, although evincing the fixed qualities of his nature, may be suddenly confronted with an opinion or a flash of inspiration hitherto entirely foreign to his beliefs. As a native of this sign, you often feel that you are being impelled by some unknown force toward new concepts or actions. These motivations are usually highly opportune and you should consider them carefully. This does not mean that you should adopt any novel idea or plan the moment it is presented. Your sign expresses advancement and accomplishment as well as persistence, and it would be to your advantage to listen to the small voice of intuition telling you to seize that opportunity.

Aquarius signifies the unusual—unusual events, people or deeds. Their names often become synonymous with their occupation or accomplishment, such as these few outstanding examples: Charles Lindbergh, aviation; Horace Greeley, journalism; Charles R. Darwin, concept of evolution; President Franklin D. Roosevelt, the New Deal; Abraham Lincoln, equal rights; Evangeline Adams, modern astrology; John L. Lewis, the labor movement; Thomas A. Edison, incandescent lighting; Thomas J. (Stonewall) Jackson, the Confederate cause in the Civil War; Douglas MacArthur, the military, and modern government for Japan; Jack Benny and Jimmy Durante, early radio entertainment.

Other Aquarians, notable in their chosen professions, include Marian Anderson and Enrico Caruso, singers; John Barrymore, Katharine Cornell and Tallulah Bankhead, theater stars; Jascha Heifetz and Fritz Kreisler, violinists; Charles Dickens, W. Somerset Maugham, and James Michener, authors; Gen. Omar N. Bradley; and Adlai Stevenson, statesman.

The characteristics of the planet Uranus are unique and the effects often electrifying. Uranus has a proclivity to break down established concepts or conditions. Although men may be aware of the need for revision of educational systems, living conditions or of existing moral standards, it often takes the impulse and the pressure of this planet to stimulate them into action.

In the zodiac, unconventional Aquarius is opposite imperious Leo, and Uranus-ruled Aquarians are often in conflict with anything that suggests bossism; Leo is ruled by the sun and it has been said that Aquarians even challenge the authority of the sun. Leo rules royalty and Aquarius acclaims universal brotherhood. These latter natives question, study and analyze everything, searching for reasons and answers to the problems of mankind. They recognize the power of knowledge as the antidote against mental, spiritual and physical ills which cause social unrest.

As an Aquarian you like to meet people and you are an interesting person to meet. Ordinarily you are kind and gentle, with charming manners and the ability to put others at ease. Some of you may be timid and reserved at times, but generally you are most expressive and quite an extrovert. If Aquarian characteristics are hard to pinpoint, it is because you are changeable and independent. You can be enthusiastic and delightful one moment and indifferent and moody the next. These latter humors are usually caused by your emotional sensitivity or to your preoccupation with some serious and pressing matters.

Because of your intuitiveness, you are especially susceptible to the feelings and needs of others, and with your Aquarian altruism, you are happiest and feel most worthy when you can be of help. Your intentions are always sincere, although at times you may act hastily or from a personal point of view. Even though your suggestions may be excellent and deserve considerations, you should be circumspect and objective in your humanitarian aims.

You have much to give; you have the ability to inspire others toward greater achievement and the persistence to help them succeed. You are equally determined in your own pursuits. No matter what your objective might be, you will see it through to final completion. Your mind is intensively active and concentrative; you are observant and you have a good memory. Some of you may be content with an overall picture of a project, but most Aquarians will remember all the details connected with it.

Aquarius is a mental sign and most of you prefer a profession or occupation which requires mental application; however, many sports notables were born under this sign. You are versatile and generally quite adaptable to circumstances or conditions. You also have a penchant for the uncommon or the unusual, and if your occupation is more or less routine and monotonous, you are quite apt to inject a note of nonconformity in your attitude toward it or in the way you do the job.

Aquarius denotes inventiveness, and many born under this sign express this ability in technical or scientific achievement (Sir Hiram Maxim, inventor of the Maxim gun), in a new and unique art from (Edouard Manet, first impressionist painter), or in a new political idea (Wendell Willkie, concept of world government).

Uranus can cause you to be temperamental; sweetness and light can give way to unpleasantness and anger, but you get over it quickly and do not hold a grudge. You are progressive and sometimes eccentric and unconventional. You may be quite domestic or you may prefer a bohemian way of life. You may be unpredictable, but you are never boring.

As a child, an Aquarian is often shy and may like to get off by himself to read or just ponder. He is easy to get along with, but inclined to worry. He has an active mind, with literary ability and inventive genius, and should be encouraged along these lines. He is perceptive, studious and persistent. He is subject to the general Aquarian diseases, especially nervous disorders and poor circulation.

The Aquarian wife is intelligent and talented. She is capable and uncomplaining about household duties. She is interested in people and likes to entertain. Emotionally, she is responsive, but not as aggressive as some signs. She is happier with a mate who is successful and with whom she has an intellectual rapport. She often suffers from varicose veins, swollen ankles and nervousness. She should take care of her skin, as it is apt to be quite sensitive. She understands and appreciates the fine arts and loves color. She often expresses her Aquarian originality in unusual and gay clothes.

The Aquarian husband is kind, generous and considerate of his family. He is not as domestic as some signs, being somewhat impersonal in marital relationships. He is broadminded and is not apt to be possessive or domineering. He needs a wife who is mentally stimulating, who shares his occupational interests and whose universal interests are compatible with his own. He is susceptible to heart weaknesses, sprained or broken ankles and ruptures. He often becomes so engrossed in what he is doing that he forgets to eat or sleep, with resulting anemia or nervous disorders.

As an Aquarian, although not as robust as some signs, you usually enjoy fairly good health. You do have your weaknesses because of your sun sign and ruling planet. In zodiacal anatomy, Aquarius rules the lower legs, including the calves and ankles, blood circulation in general. Uranus rules the nervous system, pituitary body and body electricity. Diseases or infirmities to which you may be susceptible include anemia, sprained or broken ankles, blood poisoning, heart weakness, nervous disease, cramps (in legs), varicose veins, sensitive skin, ruptures, spasms, malnutrition, physic disturbances and strictures.

Many ills are psychosomatic in origin, and the Aquarian is more apt to focus his concern on matters other than his physical state. Your interest in the metaphysical often includes healing. As Aquarius is the sign of reform, you are apt to concern yourself with new and better health measures and disease-prevention methods.

The body needs food for growth, maintenance and repair, and although as an Aquarian you eat to live rather than live to eat, it is important that you supply your body with all the vitamin and mineral essentials. Study the list below and choose a diet which is suitable to your needs. If you are allergic to some particular items you may substitute others providing the same essentials.

ESSENTIAL VITAMINS*	SOURCES
Vitamin A: for growth, night vision, cells of skin and mucous membrane	Whole milk products, seafoods, fish-liver oils, liver, lamb, green-leaf vegetables, kale, yellow vegetables and fruits with yellow flesh, salad greens, etc.
Vitamin B₁ (Thiamin): for	Whole-grain products, yeast,

* See last chapter for complete list.

ESSENTIAL VITAMINS* SOURCES

glands (thyroid),
nerves, growth and re-
pair of body tissue

eggs, liver, kidney, legumes,
kelp, okra, etc.

Vitamin B₂ (Riboflavin): helps
retard process of ag-
ing; for eyes, bowel
trouble, skin, arteries,
depression

Lean meats, liver, cheese, milk,
whole grains, salad greens,
some fruits, peanuts

Vitamin B₁₂: helps prevent anemia

Liver, meat, fish and whole
grains

Niacin: prevents pellagra, disturbances of nervous
and digestive systems

Milk, fruits, eggs, nuts, oats,
green vegetables and salads,
cheese, butter, tubers

Vitamin C (Ascorbic acid): prevents tender gums,
loose teeth, sore joints,
weakness and fatigue;
helps repair wall of
blood vessels

Citrus fruits, tomatoes, raw
cabbage, baked potato, parsley,
peppers, greens, watermelon,
etc.

Vitamin D: for bones, teeth,
nerves

Seafoods, fish liver oils, eggs,
milk, raw cabbage, cheese,
onions, etc.

Vitamin E: for fertility

Wheat germ and whole-grain
products, lettuce, bean sprouts,
fish, celery, legumes, etc.

Vitamins K₁ and K₂: to help
process of blood-clot-
ting

Green-leaf vegetables, some
grains, legumes, alfalfa herb

Vitamin P (Rutin): to
strengthen walls of
small veins, to prevent
hemorrhages

Paprika, lemon rind and some
herbs

ESSENTIAL MINERALS* SOURCES

Calcium: builds healthy bones
and teeth; helps pre-
vent breaking down
of cell walls; for blood
circulation and to
strengthen heart mus-
cles

Lean meat, bones (soup), okra,
lettuce, arrowroot, dandelion,
nettles, cheese, milk, dill, cabbage, chives, celery, etc.

Copper: for normal body function

Mixed green salads, liver, oysters, nuts, dried fruits

* See last chapter for complete list.

ESSENTIAL MINERALS*

SOURCES

Fluorine: for teeth, eyes, bones, anemia, nervousness

Whole grains, sea fish, corn, cabbage, brown rice, beets, etc.

Iodine: the thyroid chemical; relieves nervous tension; prevents high blood pressure; helps eliminate poisons

Fish and shellfish, kelp, radishes, milk, asparagus, lettuce, etc.

Iron: makes red blood; prevents anemia, fatigue; for energy and repair of the body

Lettuce, radishes, raisins, liver, mushrooms, spinach, romaine, parsley, etc.

Magnesium: alkaline and laxative; prevents constipation, insomnia, neurasthenia; for glands

Tomatoes, parsley, carrot leaves, lettuce, cabbage, turnips, eggplant, figs, etc.

Phosphorus: repairs and helps nervous system; keeps acids out of blood stream; for bones and teeth; prevents numbness; helps stimulate brain

Wheat bran, buttermilk, seafood, cheese, liver, radishes, cauliflower, cucumbers, watercress, sesame, garlic, etc.

Potassium: alkaline and laxative; for nerves, muscles, brain; helps prevent weakness of vital organs

Lettuce, celery, tomatoes, sorrel, eggplant, string beans, mushrooms, parsley, kale, etc.

Silicon: prevents mental fatigue, nervous exhaustion, infections: for eyes, nails, teeth and hair

Lettuce, asparagus, onions, spinach, rice bran, sunflower seeds, etc.

Sodium: for body repair, tissues and ligaments; aids in use of other chemicals; for bile, saliva and other body juices

Celery, watercress, cheese, carrots, lettuce, oysters, cabbage, beets, chives, etc.

Sulphur: helps enliven the whole system; removes impurities through the skin

Watercress, garlic, cabbage, kale, okra, Brussels sprouts, turnips, etc.

* See last chapter for complete list.

Herbs and spices contain many of the essential vitamins, minerals and oils needed by the body for growth and repair. They are natural foods and easy to assimilate. Some may be used as flavoring and some for medicinal purposes.

Herb teas are pleasant to the taste and more healthful than Oriental teas. Many are good at mealtime, some can be a nice pickup in the morning or afternoon, and others are relaxing when served before retiring. For the Aquarian who is subject to nervousness, may we suggest camomile, hops or linden tea. Ginger or pennyroyal teas are good for minor disturbances and much better for your health than pills. Alfalfa, being one of nature's richest sources of trace elements, makes an excellent tea.

Many of the botanicals are nourishing and easily digested. Arrowroot is a good carbohydrate and source of calcium. Carob pods contain natural sugar to satisfy the sweet tooth. Okra pods contain the B vitamins, calcium, magnesium and sulphur. Spices, although used mainly as flavoring, also contain food essentials. Paprika contains vitamins A, B, and P; and saffron, oregano, marigold and rose hips all contain vitamin C. (More herbs are listed in the last chapter.)

Since ancient times man has known of the value of various herbs and spices. Prehistoric man depended upon plants, herbs and spices to supplement his meager diet and to provide his only source of medicine. Many herbs and spices were believed to have powers of different sorts: For some twenty centuries superstitious people in continental Europe believed that if southernwood was tucked under one's mattress, it evoked sensual passions. The recipe did not state if one used a pinch or a bale of this aromatic herb. Many whole orris roots vaguely resemble human forms in seated position. They are valued according to perfection of shape. Voodoos tie thread around the neck of the figure and let the root hang. Wishes are fulfilled or rejected, according to the way the root moves. It is also mixed with other love and wooing compounds, probably for scent. An old European legend held that pillows stuffed with mugwort would reveal one's entire future in dreams.

After the invention of the printing press many of the astrologer-herbalists put their herb lists in book form. One of the best known was Nicholas Culpeper (1616–1654). The following excerpts from his book may be both interesting and valuable.

Asparagus: "The decoction of the roots boiled in wine and taken, is good to clear the sight, and being held in the mouth easeth the toothache, and being taken fasting several mornings together, stirreth up lust in man or woman . . . and no less effectual against stiff and benumbered sinews or those that are shrunk by cramps and convulsions."

Avens (herb bennet): "The decoction, being drunk, comforts the heart. It should be steeped in wine and drunk, fasting in the morning."

Bay tree: "The oil made of the berries is very comfortable in all cold griefs of the joints, nerves, arteries, and helpeth cramps, aches and trembling. The oil takes away the marks of the skin and flesh by bruises and dissolveth the congealed blood in them."

Betony (wood): "It helpeth those . . . that have a rupture. The green herb bruised, or the juice applied, helpeth the veins that are troubled. It is commended against the stinging of mad dogs or venomous serpents."

Brank Ursine: "The leaves being bruised, or rather boiled, and applied like a poultice, are very good to unite broken bones, and strengthen joints that have been put out . . . it reviveth the ends of the veins which are relaxed; this is an excellent remedy for such as have ruptures, being taken inwardly or applied to the place."

Cowslips, or Peagles: "An ointment being made of them [flowers], taketh away spots or wrinkles and adds beauty exceedingly to the skin. Because they strengthen the brain and nerves and remedy palsies, the Greeks gave them the name Paralysis."

Gladwin (Iris): "The powder drank in wine helps those that are troubled with cramps. The juice of the roots or leaves is good for the skin."

Marjoram (common wild): "It strengthens the stomach and head much. It is an excellent medicine in nervous cases. The whole plant is a warm aromatic and an infusion of the leaves is extremely grateful."

Sage (wood): "The decoction of the green herb, made with wine, is a safe and sure remedy for those who, by falls or bruises, suspect some vein to be inwardly broken."

Tormentil: "It is very powerful in ruptures and bruises and falls, used outwardly or inwardly."

Valerian: "It helps in nervous complaints, palpitations of the heart, trembling. . . ."

Pisces

(February 20–March 20)

FISH

THE PICTOGRAPH OF Pisces represents two fish bound together yet trying to proceed in different directions. They symbolize the contradictory forces at work in the consciousness, the contention between the physical and spiritual selves.

Pisces rules the twelfth house of the zodiac and is the final sign of the cycle before the new beginning. It is the sign of universal cosmic consciousness and the house of Karma, which the spirit carries with it from one life to another. It is through the twelfth house that we come face to face with our soul-consciousness. It can be the house of dissolution or solution.

This is generally known as the house of limitations, secret sorrows and self-undoing. It is also the house of mystery, of wonder, of happiness, peace and contentment. It is the most inclusive of all the signs.

Pisces is a mutable water sign, ruled by the planet Neptune. Mutable-sign natives are adaptable, conforming, comprehending, imaginative, intuitive, flexible, sympathetic and versatile. The mind is ingenious but often irresolute. Water signs are emotional, changeable, sensitive and impressionable, and often have psychical powers.

Natives of Pisces run the gamut, from the depths of escapism and despair to the heights of spiritual attainment and/or professional success.

The unevolved Piscean is evasive, undependable, subtle, vacillating and often difficult to orientate. They are insecure, refuse to face facts and will try to escape the high walls of their limitations, sometimes in aimless travel, at other times in alcohol and drugs.

The highly evolved Pisceans are the most intuitive and universal of human beings; they live as though life and love were one. They represent unity, fellowship, compassion and humanity. They know that peace of mind and contentment come from within, and the source may be hidden from the world.

Between these two classes are the countless numbers of individuals, manifesting the characteristics of their dual sign, able and well intentioned but often falling short of their material or spiritual goals.

The Piscean, if not introspective, seeks within himself a rapport between his definable awareness of earthly matters and his metaphysical reasoning. He may be philosophical or fatalistic. If he is philosophical in his approach to the problems of life, he can obtain material success and mental freedom. If, however, he bows to a tendency of this sign to be fatalistic, he may waste his talents becoming melancholic and discontented.

As a Piscean you have foresight and genius, and along with a powerful imagination you are often endowed with executive ability. You are synthetical rather than analytical. You visualize any undertaking in its entirety. To a Piscean, the beauty and the worth of an accomplishment is important, not the time or effort spent to make it so.

Many of you will work conscientiously and meticulously to perfect and conclude any project or to excel in any profession. There are, however, Pisceans who have the dream and the ability to succeed but they procrastinate until the dream is lost or they fail because they dislike the necessary detail work involved.

Such renowned Pisceans as Alexander Graham Bell, inventor of the telephone; Luther Burbank, botanist; Vannevar Bush, atomic scientist; Albert Einstein, physicist; Camille Flammarion, astronomer; Henry Wadsworth Longfellow, poet; Henrik Ibsen, playwright; Ben Hecht, novelist and dramatist; Elizabeth B. Browning, poet; Sir Edwin Landseer, painter; Augustus Saint-Gaudens, sculptor; John Steinbeck, novelist; Oliver Wendell Holmes, Supreme Court judge; Arthur Schopenhauer, philosopher; Pope Pius XII, and U.S. Presidents Grover Cleveland, Andrew Jackson, James Madison and George Washington typify the positive qualities of your sign.

Pisces is the most impressionable and receptive of all the signs, and your strong intuition helps you sense the moods of people or conditions around you. You will enjoy another's happiness with him because you want happiness and you love laughter; you will cry with him when he is sad because you feel his sorrow.

Pisces awakens compassion and an interest in the underprivileged, the confined and the burdened. The twelfth house in the zodiac rules asylums, hospitals and prisons, and you often find your own fulfillment by working in such institutions or for charity organizations. You are especially fitted for such an occupation because of your understanding and spiritual nature, and such service to mankind could be highly gratifying. You must remember to be objective, however; otherwise you would feel their troubles too deeply to be of any real help.

The symbol of Neptune, your ruling planet, is the trident and indicates the threefold nature of Man, the physical, the mental and the spiritual. Neptune is a remote, mysterious planet and it bestows an elusive, other-world quality. Its vibrations are subtle, intangible and transcendent, and only those who have attained spiritual consciousness will be able to respond to its influence.

It is known as the planet of illusion and as such has a kinship to actors, as master illusionists, or to visionary enthusiasts who create their own angels or devils. It is also the planet of confusion and, in an individual who is spiritually weak, can cause instability, uncertainty and mental unbalance.

Neptune is associated with music and musical instruments (stringed instruments in particular), with luxuries, the exotic, impressionistic and nebulous effects in art, music and literature. Inspiration from other planes assists the Piscean genius to manifest its potential. Neptune vibrations are generally prominent in the nativities of musicians, and are expressed in haunting, inspirational melodies, elusive and often sensual. Artistic and literary genius often materializes under the influence of Neptune, but as Pisces is the sign of sorrow, many natives of your sign have experienced some travail of soul before achieving greatness and were not fully appreciated until after death.

Neptune's influence is such that the native often succeeds in endeavors which are beyond the mental capacity of the average individual (Albert Einstein) and so intangible that they are never fully understood. Neptune might be termed supermental; it bestows sense perceptions of which we have little or no conception at the present time, of hazy, indefinable but often acute impressions of things we seem to know but cannot remember when or where we learned them. We call it intuition, the "still, small voice" that often advises us when to act or warns us of impending danger.

Your dual nature often makes you restless and fond of change. You like to travel and will often benefit from matters distant from your birthplace. You are likely to have many changes of residence, either from circumstances or from your own restlessness.

Ordinarily your financial status is largely up to you, depending of course on the aspects in the individual chart. Indecision and lack of confidence are negative traits of your sign that you should strive to overcome. You are imaginative, creative and often profound. Many professions and occupations are within your capabilities. You may be apprehensive about being in business for yourself, but you have the type of personality well suited for partnerships. Natives of this sign often succeed in large promotional schemes, financial, social or political.

Being so highly impressionable and receptive, you can learn anything that you want to learn, and you have an excellent memory. You store facts and impressions in your subconscious and can recall them readily. Some of the world's memory wizards were born in your sign.

Although the Piscean may be talkative, it is usually about matters other than self. He keeps his joys and his sorrows to himself; however, others will come to him with their troubles and he will be a good listener and a wise counselor. The Piscean is charming and sociable, but he needs to be alone at times.

Love affairs are apt to be numerous, because of your quick response to any emotional stimulus. You should find happiness in affairs of the heart, as you will make great personal sacrifice to protect your love. However, there are indications of secret love affairs and such involvements often lead to sorrow.

Generally the Piscean is not adapted to physical labor as he lacks the energy and strength. Since Pisces rules the feet, one might suppose that Pisceans would love to walk; however, most of you would rather drive or ride.

The Pisces child has a mental capacity beyond average and should be encouraged in any pursuit for which he shows a liking or aptitude. He is very impressionable and responds to environment and attitudes. This child needs recognition of his good points to boost his courage; disparaging remarks only tend to make him lose self-confidence. The wise parent will train him by good example rather than by force. He may be forgetful and absent-minded at times because he has a tendency to daydream. Ordinarily he is not robust and, therefore, needs special care in all matters pertaining to health.

The Pisces wife, expressing the positive qualities of the sign, is thoughtful, devoted and sympathetic. If the negative qualities predominate, she is often self-indulgent and self-seeking, interested in social affairs and arty companions. The Pisces wife's home is artistic in décor, peaceful and inviting. In marital relations the Pisces wife is adaptable, lovable and responsive. She is very sensitive and should take great care in selecting a mate.

The Pisces husband, expressing his positive qualities, is kind, thoughtful, attentive and generous. On the negative side, although generous with what he has, is not apt to be a good provider; he is uncertain, impractical and unable to face facts. The Pisces husband enjoys a certain amount of social life and fits into any group or situation with ease. His home is the place where he likes to read, listen to music and often display his artistic talents. He is sensual and seeks a wife who is affectionate and is receptive to his passions.

In zodiacal anatomy, Pisces-Neptune rules the feet, toes and their bones and muscles, the pineal gland, nerve fibers, the lymphatic process, circulation of body extremities, lachrymal gland, causes of perspiration, spinal canal, and to some extent the generative organs and the lungs. Neptune also rules superphysical or occult action, telepathic and psychometric functions.

Diseases or infirmities to which the Piscean is most susceptible include trouble with the feet, mucus discharge, gout, comas, somnambulism, poison, drug addiction and, to some extent, venereal disease, tuberculosis and heart trouble.

Pisces is a highly susceptible sign and its natives tend to take on the ailments of those with whom they come in contact. You are more high-strung and sensitive than one would suppose, and you need outlets to restore any emotional unbalance. Some outdoor activity (if only to walk), pets, gardening or a hobby are suggested. You may find that living or vacationing near water is beneficial to you. Drugs or narcotics should never be taken unless prescribed by a physician. You do need sufficient rest and properly balanced meals. Nervous tension or physical exhaustion are not conducive to good digestion and, at such times, you should eat lightly. Make it up when you are rested and calm.

The body needs food for growth, maintenance and repair. Adjust your diet so that it will suit your temperament, your build and the work you do. If specific foods disagree with you, replace them with others, but be sure that what you do eat contains all the essentials. It is easier to keep a machine, which your body is, in good running order with a small amount of care than to repair it once it breaks down. Study the food lists below and choose a diet that is appealing and also nourishing—it can be both, you know.

ESSENTIAL VITAMINS*	SOURCES
Vitamin A: for growth, night vision, cells of skin and mucous membrane; an anti-infective	Fish-liver oil (halibut), whole-milk products, eggs, spinach, lettuce, escarole, sweet potatoes, carrots, salad greens, peppers, etc.
Vitamin B₁ (Thiamine): for thyroid gland, nerves, growth and repair	Whole-grain products, yeast, legumes, lamb, milk, nuts, liver, kidney, etc.

* See last chapter for complete list.

ESSENTIAL VITAMINS*   SOURCES

Vitamin B₂ (Riboflavin): helps retard process of age; for eyes, skin, bowel trouble, mental depression
Liver, lean meats, green-leaf vegetables, whole grains, milk, raw vegetables, cheese, bananas, etc.

Vitamin B₁₂: develops red blood cells
Liver, meat, fish, whole wheat, alfalfa, etc.

Niacin: helps prevent digestive disturbances, pellagra; for nervous system
Whole oats, eggs, American cheese, most fruits, greens, etc.

Vitamin C (Ascorbic acid): for teeth, gums, bones; prevents scurvy
Citrus fruits, melons, bean sprouts, tomatoes, raw cabbage, baked potatoes, rose hips, watercress, etc.

Vitamin D: for bones, teeth; prevents rickets, nervousness and acidosis
Seafood, fish-liver oils, eggs, milk, butter, onions, wheat germ, etc.

Vitamin E: for fertility
Whole grains, celery, lean meats, lettuce, malt, fish, sweet potatoes, sesame, etc.

Vitamins K₁ and K₂: for normal blood-clotting process
Green-leaf vegetables, especially alfalfa and spinach; legumes, cabbage, etc.

Vitamin P (Rutin): to strengthen tiny blood vessels
Lemon rind, paprika and foods containing vitamin C

ESSENTIAL MINERALS*   SOURCES

Calcium: for teeth, bones, arteries
Soup bones, lettuce, cheese, cabbage, kale, watercress, okra, milk, arrowroot, etc.

Fluorine: prevents skin diseases, anemia; for eyes and teeth
Whole grains, sea fish, butter, asparagus, cabbage, garlic, etc.

Iodine: the thyroid chemical; prevents goiter, high blood pressure, nervous tendencies
All seafoods, salmon, kelp radishes, lettuce, squash

Iron: builds red blood cells; gives vitality
Lettuce, raisins, parsley, strawberries, rice bran, soup bones, spinach, asparagus, etc.

Magnesium: helps prevent constipation, neurasthenia, insomnia; alkaline and laxative
Tomatoes, carrot leaves, lettuce, sorrel, dandelion, celery, cabbage, figs, parsley, etc.

* See last chapter for complete list.

ESSENTIAL MINERALS*	SOURCES
Phosphorus: for bones and teeth, nervous system	Seafood, cheese, mushrooms, watercress, buttermilk, soy beans, liver, turnips, etc.
Potassium: builds and repairs body, muscles; alkaline and laxative	Tomatoes, nearly all vegetables, legumes, molasses, etc.
Silicon: for teeth, hair, nails; helps prevent infection, mental fatigue, nervous condition	Lettuce, horsetail grass, rice bran, asparagus, spinach, beets, onions, etc.
Sodium: builds and repairs tissue and ligaments for saliva, bile and other juices	Celery, oysters, lettuce, cheese, carrots, cabbage, etc.
Sulphur: enlivens system; an organic antiseptic	Irish moss, cabbage, okra, watercress, kale, garlic, etc.

* See last chapter for complete list.

Herbs are valuable sources of vitamins, minerals and trace elements. They may be served as a vegetable, used to add flavor to foods, or drunk as a tea. Herbs also have medicinal value, and as such have been used for centuries. Many of our "modern" medicines are decoctions of herbs. Pisces natives will find the following herbs of particular value:

Sedative: Camomile tea, hops (flowers) tea
Nervine: (to relax temporarily): Balm, valerian root, nerve root
Expectorant (to loosen phlegm of the mucous membrane): Comfrey root, elecampane, pleurisy root, horehound
Stimulant (to increase functional actions of the system): Angostura bark, ginger root, summer savory
Diaphoretic (to increase perspiration for relief of common cold): Angelica root, catnip herb, pennyroyal
For flatulence: Anise seed, fennel seed, peppermint
Cathartic: Psyllium seed

Old-time herbals, home-remedy books and health magazines listed hundreds of herbs, with their "government and virtues"—that is, the sign governing each and its medicinal value. You might find some of the following excerpts, from *Culpeper's Complete Herbal,* published in the early seventeenth century, strange and amusing.

Alehoof, or ground ivy: "The decoction, with some honey

or burnt alum, is excellent good to gargle any sore throat or mouth and to wash the sores or ulcers in the privy parts of man or woman. The decoction in wine drank for some time together easeth them that are troubled with the gout in the hands, feet or knees. The juice dropped in the ear doth wonderfully help the noise or singing of them."

Borage: "A cordial and great strengthener of nature. . . . The leaves, flowers and seed, any or all of them, are food to expel pensiveness and melancholy. The flowers candied or made into a conserve will comfort the heart and spirits of those that are in consumption. The roots are effectual, being made into a licking electuary, for the cough and to condensate phlegm, and the rheumatic distillations upon the lungs."

Bugle: "Many times such as give themselves much to drinking are troubled with strange fancies, strange sights in the night time, and some weird voices, as also with the disease ephialtes, or nightmare; these I have known cured by taking two spoonsful of the syrup of this herb after supper two hours, when you go to bed."

Colt's foot: "The fresh leaves, or juice, or syrup thereof, is good for those who have thin rheums and distillations upon their lungs: for which the dried leaves, taken as tobacco, is also good."

Garden mint: "The juice taken in vinegar stays bleeding, stirs up venery or bodily lust; two or three branches taken in the juice of four pomegranates, stays the hiccough and allays the choler. Applied with salt it helps the bites of mad dogs. Applied to the forehead it eases the pains in the head. The dried powder taken after meat helps digestion. Taken in wine it helps women in their sore travail in childbearing."

Rose (hip): "Red roses strengthen the heart, the liver and the retentive faculty; they mitigate the pains that arise from heat, cool inflammations, procure rest and sleep; the juice purges and cleanses the body from choler and phlegm. The dry conserve, which is called sugar of roses, strengthens the heart and spirits. Red rose water is well known; it is cooling, refreshing, quickening the weak and faint spirits, used either in meats or broths, to wash the temples, to smell at the nose or to smell the sweet vapours out of a perfume pot or cast into a hot fireshovel."

Drugs, opiates and narcotics are ruled by Neptune, and

nothing denotes the illusion and confusion of this planet more aptly than the various drugs. In every part of the world man came to know drugs through his search for food. He found that some of them were mildly stimulating; others had horrifying results. The purpose of drugs in nature is a mystery. Many of the modern drugs are either synthetic or decoctions of botanicals.

Among those which nature has provided, or which modern science has manufactured, we find anesthetics, mild stimulants, sexual stimulants, tranquilizers, sedatives and hallucinogens. (The reader is advised that the following information is for astrological study only and not to suggest that you experiment with some of the various sources mentioned.)

The milder stimulants, such as tea and coffee, both contain caffein, and people with heart trouble are usually advised against their use. Cocoa contains bromine, a mild stimulant. Tobacco contains nicotine, a relaxant that may bring on forgetfulness. Alcohol is a depressant. These are all habit-forming, but not addictive.

The hemp plant provides marijuana (also known as hashish). It is addictive, as is cocaine, an opiate deprived from cocoa, grown in Peru. The Incas regarded cocaine a royal drug; it gives energy and eliminates hunger.

Opium, derived from the poppy capsule, contains about twenty alkaloids, such as codeine, heroin, morphine and others. (The poppy capsule is slit and the milk that is discharged coagulates. It is scraped off and dried; this is opium.)

The root of the mescal cactus is a powerful hallucinogen, causing delirium and insomnia.

The Spaniards, searching for the Fountain of Youth (sustained sexual ability) and cities of gold were introduced to certain mushrooms growing in Mexico and Colombia. Although these mushrooms induced sexual urges, they caused the user to age twice as fast. As for the cities of gold, they were visions and hallucinations caused by the extract of certain plants. Mushroom extracts are very powerful, and modern scientists are experimenting with many, growing in South America, that seem to induce psychic power.

At such orgiastic celebrations as the Roman Saturnalia and the Greek Dionysia, extracts of certain herbs, especially belladonna and henbane, were mixed with the wine to cause release from sexual inhibitions.

Special Diet
for
Each Sign

ARIES

As noted in the chapter on Aries, your sign has certain disease tendencies. Many of these may be corrected by proper diet, stressing food elements that your system may lack. In addition, there are herbs which are particularly beneficial to natives of your sign. Some may be used as cooking herbs, others for medicinal purposes.

The individual horoscope may show a disease tendency or chemical unbalance not usually ascribed to your sign; however, the following suggested menus and medicinal herbs should help you in maintaining good health.

For the normal or underweight Aries

Breakfast

Orange juice or stewed apricots

Whole-oat cereal
Two eggs, soft-boiled or poached
Whole-wheat toast with butter and honey
Coffee (eye bright herb) or cocoa (mint)

Lunch

Vegetable-juice cocktail
Whole-wheat or corn muffin
Broiled ground beef patty
Lettuce-tomato salad
Ice cream and cookies
Coffee, milk or herb tea

Dinner

Cream of asparagus soup
Baked ham with raisin sauce
Baked sweet potatoes
Tossed green salad

For the overweight Aries

Breakfast

One half fresh-cut lemon in water or half grapefruit
One egg, hard-boiled
Two figs
Bran muffin with honey (no butter)
Black coffee or herb tea

Lunch

Apple juice
Melba toast
Cottage cheese and fruit plate
Oatmeal cookie
Buttermilk or tea (primrose herb)

Dinner

Vegetable-juice cocktail
Two grilled lamb chops (mint)
Baked potato with sour cream (chives)

For the normal or underweight Aries (continued)

(pinch of tarragon or borage)
Steamed broccoli
Sesame-seed roll
Peach cobbler
Coffee or Yerba Mate tea

Breakfast

Grapefruit-orange juice
Scrambled eggs (oregano)
Bran muffins with raisins
Guava or apple jelly
Coffee or cocoa

Lunch

Tomato juice and watercress cocktail
Tuna-fish casserole (marjoram herb)
Relish tray—celery, radish, etc.
Caraway-seed roll
Alfalfa tea or Sanka coffee

Dinner

Clam chowder (thyme)
Baked salmon (mint)
Tiny whole boiled potatoes
Green peas in butter sauce
Mixed green salad (fennel)
Apple brown Betty
Coffee or herb tea

For the overweight Aries (continued)

Asparagus tips on lettuce with low-calorie French dressing
Steamed carrots (thyme)
Pineapple sherbet
Coffee or peppermint tea with honey and lemon

Breakfast

Stewed figs
Whole-grain cereal with banana
Coffee or herb tea (boneset)

Lunch

Tomato juice and watercress cocktail
Vegetable plate with hard-boiled egg
Corn muffin
Plain jello
Alfalfa tea or Sanka coffee

Dinner

Clam broth
Broiled halibut with lemon-butter sauce
Baked squash
Lettuce-tomato salad
Apricot whip
Coffee or linden tea (lemon)

TAURUS

As noted in the chapter on Taurus, your sign has certain disease tendencies. Many of these be corrected by proper diet, stressing food elements that your system may lack. In addition, there are herbs which are of particular benefit to natives of your sign. Some may be used as cooking herbs, others for medicinal purposes.

The individual horoscope may show a disease tendency not usually ascribed to your sign; however, the following suggested menus and medicinal herbs should help you maintain good health.

For the normal or underweight Taurus

Breakfast

Orange juice or stewed figs
Whole-wheat cereal (small bowl)
Two strips bacon, one egg
Whole-wheat toast, apple jelly
Coffee (buckthorn) or cocoa (pinch of sage or fennel)

Lunch

Cup of bouillon (dash of savory)
Mixed vegetable salad with ham and cheese strips (parsley)
Rye toast
Sanka coffee or peppermint tea

Dinner

Vegetable-juice cocktail
Roast chicken
Brown rice (saffron)
Spring salad (tarragon, thyme)
Sesame-seed roll
Ice cream
Coffee (sage) or yarrow tea

Breakfast

Pineapple-grapefruit juice
Two eggs (boiled)

For the overweight Taurus

Breakfast

Grapefruit juice or one-quarter cantaloupe
One egg (hard-boiled)
Whole-wheat toast or muffin with dietetic jelly
Black coffee (buckthorn herb) or fennel tea

Lunch

Apple or prune juice
Cottage cheese with pears
Melba toast
Molasses cookies
Sanka, buttermilk or peppermint tea

Dinner

Tomato juice (dash of lemon)
Breast of roast chicken (one)
Brown rice with saffron (small portion)
Spring salad—lettuce, tomato, radishes, chickweed (tarragon)
Whole-wheat Melba toast
Lemon sherbet
Coffee or Yerba Buena tea

Breakfast

Pineapple juice
Whole-wheat cereal with one ripe banana

For the normal or underweight
Taurus (continued)

Cracked-wheat toast with sage
honey
Coffee, cocoa, or horehound tea

Lunch

Oyster stew (parsley)
American-cheese sandwich (rye
or whole-wheat toast)
Lettuce and tomato, French
dressing
Sanka or mixed-herb tea

Dinner

Shrimp cocktail or clam
chowder
Broiled halibut (pinch of sage)
Baked potato with sour cream
and chives
Spinach soufflé
Wheat rolls
Mixed salad with watercress,
radish slices, tomato, etc.
(olive oil and tarragon vine-
gar)
Spice cake
Coffee or mint tea

For the overweight Taurus
(continued)

Coffee (black) or horehound
tea

Lunch

Carrot juice
Two eggs (hard-boiled)
Sliced tomatoes (pinch of
oregano)
Soy crackers
Sanka or mixed herb tea

Dinner

Potato soup (one cup)
Steamed haddock
Spinach soufflé
Celery, radishes, carrot sticks
Wheat Melba toast
Fruit in season
Coffee or mint tea

GEMINI

As noted in the chapter on Gemini, your sign has certain
disease tendencies. Many of these may be corrected by proper
diet, stressing food elements that your system may lack. In
addition, there are herbs which are of particular benefit to
natives of your sign. Some may be used as cooking herbs,
others for medicinal purposes.

The individual horoscope may show a disease tendency not
usually ascribed to your sign; however, the following suggested menus and medicinal herbs should help you maintain
good health.

For the normal or underweight Gemini

Breakfast

Orange juice or prunes
Whole-oat cereal
Two strips crisp bacon
Two three-minute eggs
One slice toast
Coffee or cocoa (plantain) or
   wintergreen tea

Lunch

Mixed-vegetable juice
Chicken à la king, with parsley
   (serve on protein-bread
   toast)
Romaine-tomato salad with
   French dressing (basil)
Sanka or tea (bay leaf)

Dinner

French onion soup (parsley)
Baked veal cutlet (pinch of
   curry in crumbs)
Lima bean casserole (summer
   savory)
Mixed green salad (borage)
Coconut blancmange
Coffee or pennroyal tea

Breakfast

Pineapple-coconut juice
Two-egg omelet (dash of
   paprika, kelp, sweet
   marjoram)
Whole-wheat toast, apricot jam
Coffee or herb tea (betony,
   with bit of dried orange
   peel)

Lunch

Cream of celery soup or celery
   juice (parsley)

For the overweight Gemini

Breakfast

One half grapefruit
One egg, hard-boiled
Zwieback
Coffee (plantain herb)
   or wintergreen tea

Lunch

Sauerkraut juice
Vegetable plate—beets, carrots,
   spinach, one egg (hard-
   boiled)
Whole-wheat rusk
Sanka or tea (bay leaf)

Dinner

One cup bouillon
One broiled ground-beef patty
Small baked potato, sour cream
   (chives or parsley)
Sliced tomatoes (borage)
One scoop pineapple sherbet
Coffee or pennyroyal tea

Breakfast

One half lemon in water or
   stewed dried apricots
One-egg omelet (dash of kelp
   or parsley)
Wheat Melba toast
Coffee or herb tea (betony,
   with bit of dried orange
   peel

Lunch

Carrot-watercress-parsley juice
One salmon croquette

For the normal or underweight Gemini (continued)

Salmon croquettes with white sauce (sorrel)
Raw-cabbage salad
Corn muffin
Spice cake
Coffee or mixed herb tea

Dinner

Oyster stew (dash celery seed)
Broiled sole (dash parsley and bay leaf)
Stuffed baked potato (minced onion, garlic and savory)
Broccoli (butter sauce with chervil and chives)
Lettuce-tomato salad (borage)
Lemon pie, graham-cracker crust
Sanka or hops tea

For the overweight Gemini (continued)

Raw-cabbage salad, low-calorie dressing
Rye crisp
One ginger cookie
Coffee or mixed herb tea

Dinner

Clam chowder (one cup)
Broiled ocean perch (one slice, lemon slices, chopped parsley)
Mixed green salad (borage)
Melba toast
One fresh peach or pear
Sanka or hops tea

MOONCHILD (CANCER)

As noted in the chapter on Moonchild (Cancer), your sign has certain disease tendencies. Many of these may be corrected by proper diet, stressing food elements, that your system may lack. In addition, there are herbs which are of particular benefit to natives of your sign; some may be used as cooking herbs, others for medicinal purposes.

The individual horoscope may show a tendency not usually ascribed to your sign; however, the following suggested menus and medicinal herbs should help you maintain good health.

For the normal or underweight Moonchild

Breakfast

Orange juice or fresh fruit
Whole-wheat cereal

For the overweight Moonchild

Breakfast

One half lemon in water or one tangerine

For the normal or underweight Moonchild (continued)

Omelet (basil or rosemary)
Toast, clover honey
Coffee (gentian herb) or peppermint tea

Lunch

Carrot-celery-cucumber juice
Beef ragout (basil herb)
Lettuce-tomato salad
Wheat roll
Coffee (calamus herb) or slippery-elm tea

Dinner

Cream of tomato soup (dash tarragon)
Grilled lamb chops, mint sauce
Rice ring with green peas, tiny whole onions, chopped parsley
Mixed green salad (ground basil leaves)
Poppy-seed roll
Ice cream, anise-seed cookies
Sanka (pinch of gentian) or balm tea (one whole clove)

Breakfast

Pineapple juice or fruit
Scrambled eggs (kelp or parsley)
Blueberry muffins
Coffee (one sage leaf) or mixed herb tea

Lunch

Pineapple-coconut juice
Shrimp chow mein, thin noodles
Endive, escarole salad with olive oil and lemon juice dressing (chervil)
Almond cooky

For the overweight Moonchild (continued)

One egg, hard-boiled
Bran muffin, clover honey
Coffee (gentian herb) or peppermint tea

Lunch

Carrot-celery-cucumber juice
Grilled beef patty
Sliced tomatoes (burnet)
Wheat muffin
Slippery-elm tea or coffee (calamus herb)

Dinner

Tomato soup (clear), dash tarragon
One grilled lamb chop
Steamed carrots, parsley
Endive salad, low-calorie dressing (chives, dash marjoram)
Two anise-seed cookies
Sanka (pinch of gentian) or balm tea (one whole clove)

Breakfast

One half grapefruit
Whole-wheat cereal with blueberries or strawberries (no sugar)
Non-fat milk, coffee, or mixed herb tea

Lunch

Carrot-coconut juice
Cottage cheese, pineapple, two black olives, lettuce
Wheat Melba toast
Coffee (one sage leaf) or peppermint tea

For the normal or underweight Moonchild (continued)

Coffee (one sage leaf) or peppermint tea

Dinner

Fish chowder (dash savory, mace)

Broiled trout (lemon slices, chopped chervil, chives, one bay leaf)

Small whole boiled potatoes, parsley butter

Green peas (pinch of fresh mint)

Cucumbers, sour cream, onions

Sponge cake, lemon sauce

Sanka coffee (buckthorn) or balm tea

For the overweight Moonchild (continued)

Dinner

Fish chowder, small cup (dash savory and mace)

Broiled trout small portion (lemon slice, chervil, chives, bay leaf)

Mixed salad—lettuce, cucumber, tomato, radish, with olive oil, lemon juice and tarragon dressing

Sanka coffee (buckthorn) or balm tea

LEO

As noted in the chapter on Leo, your sign has certain disease tendencies. Many of these may be corrected by proper diet, stressing food elements that your system may lack. In addition, there are herbs which are of particular benefit to natives of your sign; some may be used as cooking herbs, others for medicinal purposes.

The individual horoscope may show a disease tendency not usually ascribed to your sign; however, the following suggested menus and medicinal herbs should help you maintain good health.

For the normal or underweight Leo

Breakfast

Orange or prune juice

Scrambled eggs (dash of kelp)

Crisp bacon

Protein-bread toast

Coffee (plantain herb) or primrose tea

For the overweight Leo

Breakfast

Stewed prunes (dash of lemon, no sugar)

One egg, scrambled (dash of kelp)

Bran muffin

Coffee (plantain herb) or primrose tea

For the normal or underweight
Leo (continued)

Lunch

Tomato juice, celery, radishes
Broiled lambburger (savory
  herb)
Steamed carrots (parsley, bit of
  garlic)
Rye (with caraway seeds) toast
Sherbet, cookies
Coffee (pinch of dandelion root
  herb) or burnet tea

Dinner

Green pea soup (dash of mint)
Broiled chicken
Baked squash (chervil and
  chives)
Mixed green salad (marjoram
  herb)
Sesame-seed roll
Cherry tart
Coffee (buckthorn herb) or
  hops tea

Breakfast

Pineapple juice or fruit
Omelet (chopped parsley and
  basil)
Whole-wheat toast, apple butter
Coffee (one sage leaf) or mixed
  herb tea

Lunch

Carrot-watercress juice
Scalloped tuna and potatoes
  made with celery soup
  (grated onion, paprika)
Lettuce-tomato salad, French
  dressing (borage)
Coffee (horsetail herb) or alfalfa tea

For the overweight Leo
(continued)

Lunch

Tomato juice
Celery and radishes
Cottage cheese (pinch of cara-
  way seed)
Rye Melba toast
One cup fruit cocktail (no
  sugar)
Coffee (pinch of dandelion root
  herb) or burnet tea

Dinner

Mixed vegetable juice
Broiled chicken (one half por-
  tion)
Steamed Brussel sprouts
  (savory)
Raw carrot salad
Soy crackers
One fresh pear
Coffee (buckthorn herb) or
  hops tea

Breakfast

Grapefruit juice
One egg, hard-boiled (dash
  oregano)
Wheat Melba toast
Coffee (one sage leaf) or mixed
  herb tea

Lunch

Carrot-watercress juice
Tuna salad with low-calorie
  dressing (celery, chives, dash
  mint)
Rye Krisp
Coffee (horsetail herb) or alfalfa tea

For the normal or underweight
Leo (continued)

Dinner

Cream of celery soup (dash
thyme)
Baked cod, herb sauce (basil,
thyme, marjoram)
Baked potato, parsley butter
Mixed green salad, French
dressing with tarragon,
chives, bit of mustard
Lemon custard
Sanka coffee (buckthorn) or
camomile tea

For the overweight Leo
(continued)

Dinner

Celery soup, clear
Boiled cod (boil with mixed
herbs, bay leaf, basil, tarragon and parsley)
Steamed turnip greens
(savory)
Pineapple sherbet
Sanka coffee (buckthorn) or
camomile tea

VIRGO

As noted in the chapter on Virgo, your sign has certain
disease tendencies. Many of these may be corrected by proper
diet, stressing food elements that your system may lack. In
addition, there are herbs which are of particular benefit to
natives of your sign; some may be used as cooking herbs,
others for medicinal purposes.

The individual horoscope may show a disease tendency not
usually ascribed to your sign; however, the following suggested menus and medicinal herbs should help you maintain
good health.

For the normal or underweight
Virgo

Breakfast

Prune juice or stewed prunes
Eggs, soft-boiled or poached
Wheat cereal (cooked)
Protein toast
Sage coffee or raspberry-leaf tea

Lunch

Celery-parsley juice (dash
lemon)

For the overweight Virgo

Breakfast

Prune juice (dash of lemon)
One egg, hard-boiled
Wheat toast, honey (no butter)
Sage coffee or raspberry-leaf tea

Lunch

Celery-parsley juice (dash
lemon)

For the normal or underweight Virgo (continued)

Broiled liver
Stuffed potato (minced green pepper, onion and pinch of savory)
Tomato-cauliflower salad (raw)
Sanka coffee or flaxseed tea
(If flaxseed, a laxative, is not necessary, use primrose)

Dinner

French potato soup (pinch sorrel)
Lamb stew (carrots, lima beans, with mixed herbs: savory, bay, thyme)
Mustard greens, herb butter
Salad (lettuce, green peas, mint leaves, all-purpose dressing)
Steamed fig pudding
Coffee (buckthorn) or peppermint tea

Breakfast

Grapefruit-pineapple juice
Omelet (dash paprika and kelp)
Cinnamon bun
Coffee (pinch gentian root) or primrose tea

Lunch

Mixed vegetable juice
Shrimp Supreme in ramekin (parsley and pinch of chopped chives)
String beans, butter sauce (dash savory)
Lemon pudding
Coffee or lemon-grass tea

Dinner

Mushroom soup (dash parsley)

For the overweight Virgo (continued)

Cottage cheese
Wheat Melba
Tomato-cauliflower salad (raw)
Sanka coffee or flaxseed tea

Dinner

Bean soup, one cup (thyme)
Relish tray—celery, radish, etc.
Broiled liver
Mustard greens, herb butter
Figs, fresh or stewed
Coffee (buckthorn) or peppermint tea

Breakfast

One half grapefruit or juice
One egg, scrambled (dash kelp and paprika)
Zwieback
Coffee (gentian root) or primrose tea

Lunch

Celery-parsley juice (dash lemon)
Salad, shrimp, pineapple on romaine, low-calorie French dressing
Dietetic jellos lemon or lime
Coffee or dandelion root or lemon grass tea

Dinner

Tomato soup, clear (dash parsley)

For the normal or overweight Virgo (continued)

Broiled mackerel, butter sauce (chervil)
Baked potato, sour cream (chives)
Cabbage-carrot salad (borage in all-purpose dressing)
Prune whip, spice cookies
Coffee (buckthorn) or camomile tea

For the overweight Virgo (continued)

Whitefish or haddock, steamed (sprinkle of tarragon and savory)
Peas and carrots (spray of thyme)
Lettuce with low-calorie French dressing
One fig cooky
Coffee (buckthorn) or camomile tea

LIBRA

As noted in the chapter on Libra, your sign has certain disease tendencies. Many of these may be corrected by proper diet, stressing food elements that your system may lack. In addition, there are many herbs which are of particular benefit to natives of your sign; some may be used as cooking herbs, others for medicinal purposes.

The individual horoscope may show a disease tendency not usually ascribed to your sign; however, the following suggested menus and herbs should help you maintain good health.

For the normal or underweight Libra

Breakfast

Orange juice or stewed prunes
Cream of wheat cereal
Eggs, soft boiled or coddled
Wheat toast, marmalade
Coffee (dash Oregon grape root) or sassafras bark tea

Lunch

Celery-carrot juice
Broiled beef patty
Cabbage-stuffed tomato salad

For the overweight Libra

Breakfast

One half lemon in water or unsweetened prune juice
One egg, hard-boiled
One bran muffin
Coffee (dash Oregon grape root) or sassafras bark tea

Lunch

Celery-carrot juice
Stuffed tomato salad (cottage or cream cheese, chopped cucumber and chives)

For the normal or underweight Libra (continued)

(dash thyme or savory)
Rolls
Sanka coffee (dandelion herb) or peppermint tea

Dinner

Cream of tomato soup (dash tarragon)
Baked pork chops
Baked zucchini, butter sauce (dash paprika, garlic and chopped watercress)
Romaine-tomato salad with French dressing
Strawberry Blancmange
Sanka (sage) or camomile tea

Breakfast

Baked apple
Omelet (dash of thyme)
Protein toast
Coffee (dash juniper) or juniper tea

Lunch

Tomato juice (dash lemon)
Grilled mushrooms on rye toast
Salad (lettuce, chicory, raw spinach, garlic and tarragon in dressing)
Sanka (buckthorn) or primrose tea

Dinner

Clam chowder
Broiled perch, pike or sea bass (chervil in butter sauce)
Baked potato (minced chives, paprika)

For the overweight Libra (continued)

Rye Melba
Sanka coffee (dandelion herb) or peppermint tea

Dinner

Tomato soup, clear (tarragon)
Small broiled steak (no fat)
Steamed beets and tops (chopped parsley, chives)
Wheat roll
Sherbet
Sanka (sage) or camomile tea

Breakfast

Tomato juice (dash lemon)
One egg, scrambled (dash thyme)
Zwieback
Coffee (dash juniper) or juniper tea

Lunch

Carrot-coconut juice
Fruit plate: pears, pineapple, prunes, cottage cheese
Wheat Melba
Sanka (buckthorn) or primrose tea

Dinner

Celery soup, clear
Boiled fish, haddock or sea trout (with fennel)
Lettuce-tomato-asparagus salad, low-calorie French dressing
Lemon sherbet

For the normal or underweight Libra (continued)

Lettuce-tomato-asparagus salad (all-purpose dressing with borage)
Lemon pudding
Sanka coffee (dandelion) or peppermint tea

For the overweight Libra (continued)

Sanka coffee (dandelion) or peppermint tea

SCORPIO

As noted in the chapter on Scorpio, your sign has certain disease tendencies. Many of these may be corrected by proper diet, stressing food elements that your system may lack. In addition, there are herbs which are of particular benefit to your sign; some may be used as cooking herbs, others for medicinal purposes.

The individual horoscope may show a disease tendency not usually ascribed to your sign; however, the following suggested menus and herbs should help you maintain good health.

For the normal or underweight Scorpio

Breakfast

Apricot juice or stewed apricots
Oat cereal (cooked)
Poached eggs
Protein toast
Coffee (pinch buckthorn) or nettle tea

Lunch

Carrot-watercress juice
Stuffed green pepper: ground beef, rice (chopped parsley)
Lettuce-tomato salad, French dressing

For the overweight Scorpio

Breakfast

One half lemon in water or stewed apricots (no sugar)
One egg, hard-boiled
Bran muffin
Coffee (pinch buckthorn) or nettle tea

Lunch

Carrot-watercress juice
One broiled ground-beef patty
Sliced tomatoes (pinch oregano)
Sanka (pinch dandelion root) or Tilia tea

For the normal or underweight Scorpio (continued)

Sanka coffee (pinch dandelion root) or Tilia tea

Dinner

Green pea soup (pinch mint)
Grilled lamb chops (minced garlic, fenugreek and paprika)
Baked squash, herb butter
Cabbage-carrot salad
Lime or lemon pie with graham-cracker crust
Sanka coffee with (sage) or sage tea

Breakfast

Orange juice or fresh fruit
Omelet (pinch kelp)
Whole-wheat toast
Coffee (pinch gentian root) or boneset tea

Lunch

Beet juice, including tops (dash tarragon)
Salmon and rice loaf (pinch sage, garnish sorrel herb)
Sanka coffee or alfalfa tea

Dinner

Clam chowder (dash thyme)
Broiled fish—sole (mace) or trout (fennel)
Parsley potatoes
Mixed green salad
Steamed broccoli, lemon-butter sauce
Fig whip
Sanka coffee (one crushed coriander seed) or slippery-elm tea

For the overweight Scorpio (continued)

Dinner

Celery soup, clear (dash chervil)
One grilled lamb chop (minced garlic, fenugreek, paprika)
Salad greens, oil and lemon juice dressing (basil and tarragon)
Sanka and (sage) or sage tea
Dietetic lime Jello

Breakfast

One fourth cantaloupe
One egg, scrambled (pinch kelp)
Bran muffin
Coffee (pinch gentian root) or boneset tea

Lunch

Mango or papaya juice
Salad plate—cottage cheese, pears, prunes
Wheat Melba
Sanka coffee or papaya-mint tea

Dinner

Tomato soup, clear (dash tarragon)
Stewed fish—haddock (fennel) or salmon (mint)
Endive-escarole salad (dash chervil)
Apple snow
Sanka coffee or slippery-elm tea

SAGITTARIUS

As noted in the chapter on Sagittarius, your sign has certain disease tendencies. Many of these may be corrected by proper diet, stressing food elements that your system may lack. In addition, there are herbs which are of particular benefit to natives of your sign; some may be used as cooking herbs, others for medicinal purposes.

The individual horoscope may show a disease tendency not usually ascribed to your sign; however, the following suggested menus and herbs should help you maintain good health.

For the normal or underweight Sagittarian

Breakfast

Orange or grape juice
Wheat cereal (cooked)
Eggs, soft-boiled or poached
Protein toast
Coffee (pinch dandelion root) or primrose tea

Lunch

Mixed vegetable juice (watercress)
Scalloped ham, carrots, potatoes (dash of savory, parsley garnish)
Endive-escarole salad (pinch of tarragon in French dressing)
Sanka coffee or thyme tea (dash lemon)

Dinner

Cream of asparagus soup
Baked chicken with brown rice (saffron)
Steamed Swiss chard or spinach (chopped chives, parsley)

For the overweight Sagittarian

Breakfast

One half lemon in water or grapefruit juice
One egg, hard-boiled
Zwieback
Coffee (pinch dandelion root) or primrose tea

Lunch

Carrot-watercress juice
Cottage cheese and fruit mold (in gelatin) with lemon French dressing
Rye Melba
Sanka coffee or peppermint tea

Dinner

Tomato soup, clear (pinch tarragon)
Small serving of baked or roasted chicken
Mixed salad: romaine, beets, carrots, cucumbers, with

For the normal or underweight Sagittarian (continued)

Salad: carrot, celery, green peppers, French dressing (pinch thyme)
Light dessert—baked pear or fresh fruit
Sanka coffee or peppermint tea

Breakfast

Orange juice or fresh fruit
Eggs, omelet or scrambled (dash thyme)
Whole-wheat toast
Coffee (pinch gentian root) or sarsaparilla tea

Lunch

Celery soup or mixed vegetable juice
Tuna or salmon loaf (mint garnish)
Salad plate: tomatoes, cucumber, green pepper rings, French dressing
Corn muffin
Sanka coffee or alfalfa tea

Dinner

Fish chowder (tarragon, thyme, pinch saffron)
Broiled cod, halibut or salmon with lemon butter or tartar sauce
Baked squash (dash savory, sage, thyme)
Tomato, cooked asparagus, pearl onions on lettuce, French dressing
Lemon pudding
Sanka coffee (pinch camomile herb) or camomile tea (pinch ginger)

For the overweight Sagittarian (continued)

low-calorie French dressing (sprinkle borage)
Sherbet
Sanka coffee or sassafras-bark tea

Breakfast

One half grapefruit
Bran flakes with skim milk and raw sugar
One egg
Sanka coffee or mixed herb tea

Lunch

Celery-parsley juice (dash lemon)
Stuffed tomato: shrimp or tuna salad (watercress)
Rye Melba
Sanka coffee or alfalfa tea

Dinner

Celery soup, clear (pinch thyme)
Steamed haddock or whitefish with lemon slices
Tomato, cooked asparagus pearl onions on lettuce, low-calorie French dressing
One corn muffin
Fresh fruit: berries, pear, apple or grapes
Sanka coffee (pinch camomile herb) or camomile tea (pinch ginger)

CAPRICORN

As noted in the chapter on Capricorn, your sign has certain disease tendencies. Many of these may be corrected by proper diet, stressing food elements that your system may lack. In addition, there are herbs which are of particular benefit to natives of your sign; some may be used as cooking herbs, others for medicinal purposes.

The individual horoscope may show a disease tendency not usually ascribed to your sign; however, the following suggested menus and herbs should help you maintain good health.

For the normal or underweight Capricorn

Breakfast

Fruit juice or fresh fruit
Cream of Wheat or Cream of Rice
Eggs, poached
Protein toast
Coffee (pinch gentian root) or rosemary tea

Lunch

Carrot-celery-parsley juice
Herb meat loaf with cheese strips (basil, rosemary and savory)
Cauliflower in butter sauce
Sanka coffee or sweet woodruff tea

Dinner

Green pea soup (dash mint)
Baked ham with pineapple slices
Steamed French endive, herb butter
Baked yams
Caraway-seed rolls
Salad bowl (few fennel leaves)

For the overweight Capricorn

Breakfast

One half lemon in water or one half grapefruit
One egg, hard-boiled
Bran muffin
Coffee (pinch gentian root) or rosemary tea

Lunch

Carrot-celery-parsley juice
Mixed green salad (few dill leaves)
Sliced American cheese, rye Melba
Sanka coffee or chickweed tea

Dinner

Potato soup
Caraway-seed crackers
Broiled ground beef patty
Steamed carrots (dash thyme)
Salad bowl (chickweed)
Sanka (one sage leaf) or sage tea

For the normal or underweight Capricorn (continued)

Fig whip
Sanka (one sage leaf) or sage tea

Breakfast

Fruit juice or stewed figs
Eggs, omelet or scrambled
Wheat toast, honey
Coffee (pinch gentian root) or mixed herb tea (skull-cap)

Lunch

Tomato soup (tarragon and ground basil)
Crab meat—vegetable casserole
Celery in cream sauce (chopped chervil or parsley)
Green salad (dill, rosemary leaves)
Sanka or coffee substitute or fennel-seed tea

Dinner

Fish chowder (dash tarragon)
Broiled fish, herb butter sauce (few chopped leaves burnet, dill, sorrel)
Baked potato, parsley butter or sour cream and chives
Steamed Brussels sprouts
Head lettuce, cucumber, French dressing
Sanka coffee (pinch buckthorn) or peppermint tea

For the overweight Capricorn (continued)

Breakfast

Grapefruit juice or one quarter cantaloupe
Seven-grain cereal, honey or raw sugar, skim milk
Coffee (pinch gentian root) or sweet woodruff tea

Lunch

Carrot-cabbage juice (dash parsley)
Egg salad-stuffed tomato
Celery, radishes, green onions
Wheat Melba toast
Sanka or coffee substitute or fennel-seed tea

Dinner

Celery soup, clear (dash thyme)
Steamed haddock or cod, butter sauce (few chopped leaves burnet, dill, sorrel)
Salad bowl: lettuce, raw spinach, watercress, radishes, grated carrot, lemon French dressing
Soy crackers or wheat Melba
Sanka coffee (pinch buckthorn) or peppermint tea

AQUARIUS

As noted in the chapter on Aquarius, your sign has certain disease tendencies. Many of these may be corrected by proper diet, stressing food elements that your system may lack. In addition, there are herbs which are of particular benefit to natives of your sign; some may be used as cooking herbs, others for medicinal purposes.

The individual horoscope may show a disease tendency not usually ascribed to your sign; however, the following suggested menus and herbs should help you maintain good health.

For the normal or underweight Aquarian

Breakfast

Papaya juice (alkaline) or figs
Cream of wheat cereal
Protein toast
Eggs, poached or soft-boiled
Coffee (one sage leaf) or primrose tea

Lunch

Celery soup or celery-parsley juice (drop of lemon)
Chicken salad or chicken pie with vegetables (parsley garnish)
Wheat rolls
Apricot whip
Sanka coffee (pinch eyebright herb) or balm tea

Dinner

Cream of asparagus soup
Roast leg of lamb (rub with sweet marjoram and savory), mint sauce
Baked squash, green peas (dash basil)
Endive-escarole salad (tarragon, burnet)
Strawberry mousse
Sanka coffee (one coriander seed) or peppermint tea

For the overweight Aquarian

Breakfast

One half lemon in water or unsweetened grapefruit juice
One egg, hard-boiled
Wheat rusk
Coffee (one sage leaf) or primrose tea

Lunch

Carrot-coconut juice
Salad plate: cottage cheese, lettuce, pears
Protein Melba toast
One whole-wheat molasses cooky
Sanka (pinch eyebright herb) or balm tea

Dinner

Celery soup (clear)
Roast lamb (rub with sweet marjoram, savory), chopped mint leaves
Steamed broccoli, lettuce, tomato salad (oil, lemon juice, tarragon)
Sherbet
Sanka coffee or peppermint tea

For the normal or underweight Aquarian (continued)

Breakfast

Mango juice or cantaloupe
Eggs, omelet or scrambled
 (dash kelp, rosemary, basil)
Wheat toast
Coffee (pinch horsetail herb),
 cocoa or sassafras tea

Lunch

Mixed vegetable juice
Crab meat salad, or crab-vege-
 table casserole
Wheat roll
Sherbet or light pudding
Coffee or Sanka (pinch gentian
 herb) or alfalfa-mint tea

Dinner

Tomato juice dash lemon,
 (minced green fennel)
Broiled lobster, herb butter
 (chives, parsley, watercress)
String beans (minced garlic,
 onion, pinch summer savory)
Mixed green salad: sorrel, let-
 tuce, dandelion leaves, etc.,
 French dressing
Dinner rolls
Light dessert
Coffee or Sanka or linden tea

For the overweight Aquarian (continud)

Breakfast

One half grapefruit
One egg (dash kelp, rosemary,
 basil)
Bran muffin
Coffee (pinch horsetail herb)
 or chickweed tea

Lunch

Celery-parsley juice (drop
 lemon)
Stuffed tomato with tunafish
 salad on lettuce
Wheat Melba toast
Coffee or Sanka (pinch gentian
 herb) or alfalfa-mint tea
Dietic Jello

Dinner

Tomato juice (dash lemon,
 minced green fennel)
Broiled lobster (average serving only 88 calories)
Steamed carrots (dash of garlic,
 minced parsley)
Mixed green salad: sorrel, lettuce, dandelion leaves, etc.,
 low-calorie French dressing
Sherbet
Coffee or Sanka or linden tea

Before retiring: Camomile or elder-flowers tea

PISCES

As noted in the chapter on Pisces, your sign has certain disease tendencies. Many of these may be corrected by proper diet, stressing food elements that your system may lack. In addition, there are herbs which are of particular benefit to your sign. Some may be used as cooking herbs, others for medicinal purposes.

The individual horoscope may show a disease tendency not usually ascribed to your sign; however, the following suggested menus and herbs should help you maintain good health.

For the normal or underweight Pisces

Breakfast

Orange or prune juice
Whole-grain cereal
Eggs (pinch oregano or paprika)
Raisin-bread toast
Coffee, cocoa or comfrey tea

Lunch

Mixed vegetable juice
Grilled beef patty (garlic salt)
Steamed carrots (pinch thyme)
Lettuce-cucumber-tomato salad (pinch basil on tomato, French dressing)
Caraway-seed roll
Coffee or Sanka (one sage leaf) or alfalfa tea

Dinner

Cream tomato soup (dash tarragon)
Roast chicken or turkey with brown-rice stuffing (sage, thyme, savory, chopped parsley)
Asparagus tips on lettuce (French dressing)
Applesauce spice cake
Coffee or Sanka (plantain, camomile) or balm tea

For the overweight Pisces

Breakfast

Grapefruit juice or one half grapefruit
One egg (pinch oregano or paprika)
Bran muffin
Coffee, cocoa or comfrey tea

Lunch

Carrot-watercress juice
One grilled beef patty (garlic salt)
Lettuce-tomato-cucumber salad (pinch basil on tomato, low-calorie dressing)
Coffee or Sanka (one sage leaf or alfalfa tea

Dinner

Tomato soup, clear (dash tarragon)
Sliced roast chicken
Steamed carrots and peas (thyme)
Green salad: lettuce, raw spinach, watercress, etc., lemon juice, oil
Apple snow
Coffee or Sanka (plantain, camomile) or balm tea

For the normal or underweight
Pisces (continued)

Breakfast

Orange juice
Rice cereal
Blueberry muffin
Eggs (dash kelp and basil or
  parsley)
Coffee or Sanka (dash dande-
  lion root) or slippery-elm tea

Lunch

Mixed vegetable juice cocktail
Creamed shrimp and mush-
  rooms on toast
Shredded raw cabbage and carrot salad
Coffee or Sanka (pinch gentian
  root) or basil herb tea

Dinner

Clam chowder (dash tarragon
  or thyme)
Broiled salmon (chopped mint)
  or broiled sole (dash mace)
Small whole boiled potatoes
  (parsley)
Steamed broccoli, butter sauce
Mixed green salad (pinch of
  rue in all-purpose dressing)
Lemon pudding
Coffee or Sanka (pinch plan-
  tain) or sweet marjoram tea

For the overweight Pisces
(continued)

Breakfast

One half lemon in water, or figs
One egg (dash kelp and basil
  or parsley)
Zwieback
Coffee (buckthorn herb) or
  slippery-elm tea

Lunch

Carrot-coconut juice
Fruit salad plate with cottage
  or cream cheese
Wheat Melba toast
Coffee or Sanka (pinch gentian
  root) or basil herb tea

Dinner

Potato soup (chopped parsley)
Steamed cod or haddock (sage,
  bay leaf, rosemary, tarragon)
Mixed salad; romaine, tomato,
  radish, celery, etc.
Dietetic lime Jello
Coffee or Sanka (pinch plantain
  herb) or sweet marjoram tea

Before retiring; a mixed herb tea or catnip or camomile tea

Healthful Hints
for
All Signs

HERB TEAS (or Additives) AND MEDICINAL PROPERTIES

Agar-agar: A demulcent and mild cathartic. One teaspoonful to a cup.

Alfalfa: A healthful tea; contains vitamins and trace elements.

Anise seed: An aromatic, a carminative; for stomach. A scant teaspoonful to a cup.

Balm: For colds. One teaspoonful to a cup; add a pinch of rosemary or a few cloves.

Basil: A gourmet drink. Aids circulation. Try a pinch in Oriental tea.

Betony: A nervine (relaxant). Add a bit of dried orange peel.

Boneset: For head colds and throat; increases functional actions of system.

Borage: A refrigerant (cooling beverage).

Buckthorn: A mild cathartic. A pinch in coffee, or as a coffee substitute.

Burnet: A refrigerant. For nervousness, mental depression.

Calamus: For nervousness, acid stomach. Boil pinch in water, add to coffee.

Camomile: A calmative or nervine. As an afternoon tea, add dash of ginger, or two parts camomile, one fennel seed. Serve warm before retiring for restful sleep.

Caraway seed: An aromatic, a carminative. One teaspoonful to a cup before meals.

Cardamon seed: An aromatic, a carminative. One or two seeds in coffee or Sanka.

Catnip: A calmative, a nervine. Drink warm before retiring.

Celery seed: An aromatic, a carminative; eliminates gas, acid. One teaspoonful to a cup.

Chickweed: To purify blood (good for reducing). One full teaspoon to a cup.

Cinnamon bark: An aromatic, a carminative; to expel gas from stomach and intestines.

Comfrey root: A demulcent; for minor irritations of throat, coughs.

Coriander seed: An aromatic, a carminative. Add one seed to cocoa, coffee, etc.

Damiana herb: A stimulant. Brew as a tea.

Dandelion root: A tonic; assists process of digestion. One tea-
                  spoonful to a cup as a tea, or a pinch in coffee,
                  Sanka or cocoa.

Elder flowers: A diaphoretic, for relief of common cold. Drink
                  warm before retiring.

Eyebright: For the eyes. Steep one teaspoonful with same
                  of camomile.

Fennel seed: An aromatic, a calmative, taken as warm tea
                  before retiring. With sage for throat trouble.

Fenugreek: An excellent tea if coffee and Oriental teas are
                  prohibited.

Flaxseed: A demulcent; soothing for minor sore throat.
                  Add pinch of licorice root and teaspoonful of
                  lemon juice.

Gentian: Bitter tonic and aid to digestion. A pinch in
                  coffee or as a tea, one pinch to cup of water.

Ginger: A stimulant; to help increase functional actions
                  of system; for upset stomach; also, as a warm-
                  ing tea when chilled by exposure.

Hops: A bitter tonic; improves appetite and aids di-
                  gestion. A calmative if taken warm before re-
                  tiring.

Horehound: An expectorant; to help loosen phlegm in mu-
                  cous membranes of bronchial and nasal pas-
                  sages. Also, as hot tea at bedtime.

Juniper: For kidney disorders. A small pinch in coffee
                  or made as a tea.

Licorice root: A demulcent, an expectorant; to relieve minor
                  irritations of the throat; to loosen phlegm in
                  mucous membranes. May be used hot or cold.

Linden flowers: A calmative. A scant teaspoonful to a cup. As
                  warm tea upon retiring.

Nettles: A refreshing tea containing minerals—calcium,
                  iodine, iron, etc.

Oregon grape   To tone up system and for liver. A pinch to a
root: cup, as a tea, or may be added to coffee, Sanka,
                  etc.

Papaya leaf: Provides vitamin C. One teaspoonful to a cup.

Parsley tea: Good source of vegetable iron, iodine and trace
                  elements.

Peppermint: A wholesome tea; good for digestion. Heaping
                  teaspoonful to a cup.

Plantain: Good source of minerals—calcium, fluorine,
                  sulphur, etc. One teaspoonful to a cup.

Primrose: A calmative; for nerves and thus an aid to
                  digestion. One-half teaspoonful to a cup.

Rose hips: Excellent source of vitamin C. Heaping tea-
                  spoonful to a cup.

Sage:	A wholesome herb (the youth herb). A pinch of ground herb or one sage leaf added to coffee, Sanka, etc., or made as a tea.
Sarsaparilla:	A stimulant; to increase functional actions of the system.
Sassafras:	A good springtime herb tea to clear blood; also for toxic headaches and uric acid. One level teaspoonful to cup.
Slippery-elm bark:	A demulcent, an expectorant; to loosen phlegm of the mucous membranes. One teaspoonful to a cup.
Sorrel:	High chemical content, especially copper—for energy. One teaspoonful to a cup.
Strawberry leaves:	High in iron. Good alkaline substitute for tea and coffee. One teaspoonful to a cup.
Thyme:	Good for acid stomach. One teaspoonful to a cup.
Tilia flowers:	For nervous tension. One teaspoonful to a cup.
Wintergreen:	A mild stimulant; to increase functional actions of system. Heaping teaspoonful to a cup.

(Herb teas should be sweetened with honey or brown sugar.)

COOKING HERBS AND SPICES

Herb or Spice	Vitamin								Mineral					
	A.	B.	C.	D.	Cal.	Flu.	Mag.	Io.	Ir.	Phos.	Pot.	Sod.	Sil.	Sul.
Alfalfa herb	✕	✕										✕		
Anise seed												✕		
Caraway seed			✕						✕					
Celery seed												✕		
Chilies	✕	✕												
Chives			✕						✕			✕		
Coriander seed	✕		✕						✕					
Cumin	✕		✕						✕					
Dill	✕		✕		✕	✕			✕	✕				
Fennel seed									✕	✕				✕
Fenugreek		✕												
Garlic			✕			✕								✕
Horseradish	✕	✕							✕				✕	
Mustard							✕							✕
Oregano		✕												
Paprika	✕	✕												
Parsley	✕	✕	✕						✕					
Poppy seed				✕					✕				✕	
Rose hips		✕												
Saffron	✕													
Sesame											✕	✕		
Summer savory											✕			

(Alfalfa also contains vitamin E, garlic contains hormones, and parsley also contains niacin.)

A bouquet garni—a combination of herbs, such as basil, thyme, marjoram, bay-leaf and savory, either tied together or put loosely in a cheesecloth bag—will add flavor to stews and will add vitamins and minerals, as will garlic, onions, oregano and a dash of crushed chili peppers in spaghetti sauce.

FRESH VEGETABLES

The relish tray can be good health insurance:

Carrot sticks provide vitamin A, sodium and carbon.

Celery contains vitamins A, B, C and E, calcium, carbon, magnesium, nickel, potassium and sodium.

Green onions contain vitamins C and D, calcium, carbon, iron, nickel and silicon.

Olives (green) contain manganese and potassium.

Olives (ripe) contain vitamins A, B_1 and B_2, calcium and iron.

Radishes contain vitamins A, B, and C, calcium, iodine, iron, chlorine, phosphorus, potassium, magnesium, nickel and sodium.

Green or red peppers (raw) contain vitamins A, C and D.

Salad ingredients—*raw*—provide many health essentials

Beets: Chlorine, iron, manganese and sodium.

Cucumbers: Iron, magnesium, phosphorus, silicon and sodium.

Cabbage: Vitamins B, C and D, calcium, chlorine, iodine, magnesium, sodium and sulphur.

Endive: Vitamin A.

Escarole: Vitamin A.

Lettuce: Vitamins A, B_2 and E, calcium, copper, iodine, iron, magnesium, chlorine, potassium, nickel, manganese, silicon and sodium.

Tomatoes: Vitamins C and D, chlorine, iron, magnesium, nickel, potassium and sodium.

Watercress: Vitamins C and E, calcium, potassium, phosphorus, sodium, sulphur.

MEDICINAL HERBS FOR EACH SIGN

It would be impossible in this book to prescribe medicinal herbs for each individual, because each horoscope is different. The planetary placements in the individual horoscope often account for disease tendencies not usually ascribed to a particular sign. Natives of each sign, however, often find that they are especially susceptible to ailments of certain other signs. The opposing sign and the two signs which square it are often the cause of such tendencies.

For example, the sign Aries is opposed by Libra and squared by both Moonchild (Cancer) and Capricorn; thus, the Aries native may be susceptible not only to the disease tendencies of his own sign, but those of the opposing and square signs.

ARIES

Your sign:
 Head colds–catarrh, mucous discharges: boneset, colt's foot, comfrey, marshmallow root
 Insomnia: betony, camomile, Tilia flowers, valerian
 Weak or watery eyes: eyebright, fennel
Square sign (Moonchild–Cancer):
 Stomach disorders: anise seed, bay leaf, buckbean, ginger, peppermint
Opposition sign (Libra):
 Kidney trouble: juniper berries, parsley root
Square sign (Capricorn):
 Skin eruptions: chickweed, marjoram, yellow dock

TAURUS

Your sign:
 Sore throat: flaxseed, horehound, licorice root, slippery-elm bark, Solomon's seal root
 Goiter: Irish moss, kelp
 Glandular swelling: sea oak
 Obesity (herbs for reducing): burdock, elder root
Square sign (Leo):
 Heart weakness: lavender
 Fainting spells: pimpinella, coriander, veronica
Opposition sign (Scorpio):
 Elimination: buckthorn, psyllium seed
 Bladder trouble: corn silk herb, parsley herb

Square sign (Aquarius):
  Impure blood: sassafras bark, spikenard
  Circulation: basil, gentian

GEMINI

Your sign:
  Chest weakness, bronchitis: comfrey, licorice root, wild
    cherry bark
  Nervousness: betony herb, nerve root, hops flowers
  Neuritis: wintergreen
  Lungs: hyssop, ribwort
  Anemia: nettles, dandelion root
Square sign (Virgo):
  Digestive and intestinal disturbances: caraway seed, golden-
    seal root, peppermint, woodruff herb
Opposition sign (Sagittarius):
  Liver trouble: dandelion, Oregon grape root
  Rheumatic trouble: sarsaparilla, black cohosh
Square sign (Pisces):
  Colds, mucus discharge: elecampane root, gum arabic, colt's
    foot, mullein herb, comfrey root

MOONCHILD (CANCER)

Your sign:
  Digestive ailments: anise seed, bay leaves, celery seed, cin-
    namon bark, ginger root, peppermint herb, etc.
  Dropsy: dwarf elder
  Hypersensitivity: catnip herb, melissa herb, nerve root
Square sign (Libra):
  Kidney trouble: juniper berries, corn silk herb
Opposition sign (Capricorn):
  Skin: chickweed, shepherd's purse, yellow dock
  Weak constitution: dandelion root, nettles herb, plantain
Square sign (Aries):
  Head colds, mucus discharge: asafetida gum, colt's foot,
    maidenhair fern herb, comfrey root
  Weak or watery eyes: eyebright, fennel

LEO

Your sign:
> *Heart (fainting spells):* lavender
> *Heart (weakness):* coriander seed, American valerian, pimpinella, sweet basil
> *Weak eyes:* dill, plantain, watercress
> *Fevers:* linden flowers, pennyroyal
> *Throat and bronchial trouble due to heart:* colt's foot, licorice root

Square sign (Scorpio):
> *Elimination:* barberry bark, buckthorn, psyllium seed

Opposition sign (Aquarius):
> *Blood disorders:* burdock, rest harrow, sassafras root, yellow dock

Square sign (Taurus):
> *Laryngitis, tonsillitis:* flaxseed, quince seed, slippery-elm bark

VIRGO

Your sign:
> *Digestive, intestinal disturbances:* caraway seed, goldenseal root, peppermint herb, ginger root, cumin seed, wormwood
> *Malnutrition:* American centaury root, dandelion root, Irish moss, sorrel, strawberry leaves (herb)

Square sign (Sagittarius):
> *Liver trouble:* cleavers, Oregon grape root
> *Rheumatism:* black cohosh, sarsaparilla

Opposition sign (Pisces):
> *Mucous discharge:* colt's foot, comfrey, gum arabic, mullein herb, marshmallow root

Square sign (Gemini):
> *Chest weakness:* hyssop, ribwort, pleurisy root
> *Nervousness:* camomile, betony herb, hops flowers

LIBRA

Your sign:
  Kidney trouble: corn silk (herb), juniper berries, parsley root, wild carrot herb, buchu leaves herb
  Diabetes: huckleberry leaves (herb)
  Uric acid: knot grass
  Lumbago: damiana herb, goldenrod (herb), sarsaparilla root
Square sign (Capricorn):
  Teeth, bones: carragen, plantain, horsetail grass, rest harrow
  Skin troubles: chickweed, shepherd's purse, yellow dock
Opposition sign (Aries):
  Head colds: boneset, comfrey root, elecampane, sage, senega root
Square sign (Moonchild–Cancer):
  Gastric ailments: anise seed, cinnamon bark, ginger root, peppermint herb, thyme

SCORPIO

Your sign:
  Elimination afflictions: Agar-agar, blue flag root, buckthorn, butternut bark, psyllium seed, rhubarb root
  Bladder trouble: corn silk herb, parsley root, wild carrot herb
  Generative organs (inflamed): slippery elm, cramp bark
Square sign (Aquarius):
  Blood circulation ailments: basil, burdock root, elder root, gentian, red raspberry leaves (herb)
Opposition sign (Taurus):
  Throat trouble: horehound, licorice root, quince seed, slippery-elm bark, wild cherry bark
Square sign (Leo):
  Heart (nervous tension): American valerian, camomile, coriander seed, Tilia flowers, sweet basil, pimpernel
  Weak spine: dulse, Irish moss, horsetail, nettles, plantain

SAGITTARIUS

Your sign:

Rheumatism: black cohosh, celery seed, knot grass, sarsaparilla

Liver ailments: cleavers, dandelion root, liverwort, Oregon grape root

Tendency to overweight: burdock, elder root

Square sign (Pisces):

Mucous discharge (from colds): colt's foot, comfrey root, elecampane, maidenhair fern herb, gum arabic

Opposition sign (Gemini):

Chest weaknesses: blood root, hyssop, pleurisy root, ribwort

Nervousness: catnip, nerve root, valerian root

Square sign (Virgo):

Digestive, intestinal trouble: goldenseal root, peppermint herb, cumin seed, ginger root, wormwood

CAPRICORN

Your sign:

Skin diseases: chickweed, marjoram, shepherd's purse, yellow dock

Articular rheumatism: black cohosh, celery seed, kelp, knot grass, sarsaparilla root

Bones and teeth: carrageen, horsetail grass, calamus, meadow sweet flowers, nettles, rest harrow

Square sign (Aries):

Head colds: boneset, colt's foot, comfrey, rosemary, pennyroyal, sage herb

Opposition sign (Moonchild):

Digestive troubles: anise seed, caraway seed, cinnamon bark, ginger root, peppermint herb, woodruff

Square sign (Libra):

Kidney disorders: cornsilk herb, juniper berries, European goldenrod, parsley root, wild carrot herb

AQUARIUS

Your sign:

Blood circulation: basil, gentian, red raspberry leaf (herb)

Blood conditioning: alfalfa, bladderwrack, American spikenard, dulse, nettles, strawberry leaves (herb), sassafras
bark

Cramp: horsetail herb, sunflower seed

Sensitive skin (external lotions): heal-all herb, St. John's
wort, sweet fern herb, witch hazel twigs

Nervousness: betony herb, camomile flowers, nerve root,
skullcap

Square sign (Taurus):

Throat trouble: arrowroot, gum arabic, flaxseed, licorice
root, marshmallow root, slippery elm

Opposition sign (Leo):

Heart: coriander seed, sweet basil, valerian, veronica

Square sign (Scorpio):

Bladder disorder: cornsilk herb, wild carrot tops

Poor elimination: buckthorn, psyllium seed, rhubarb root

PISCES

Your sign:

Mucous discharge, colds: asafetida gum, balm gilead buds,
colt's foot, flaxseed, bloodroot, mullein herb, licorice

Cold feet: sweet marjoram herb tea, hayflower foot baths

Feet—poor bone structure: carrageen, dandelion root, nettles, calamus, meadowsweet, toad flax

Square sign (Gemini):

Chest weaknesses: borage, comfrey, ribwort, hyssop, wild
cherry bark, senega root

Opposition sign (Virgo):

Digestive, intestinal disorders: goldenseal root, peppermint
herb, ginger root, wormwood

Square sign (Sagittarius):

Liver trouble: dandelion, Oregon grape root, liverwort

Gout: barberry bark, butternut bark, broom tops, psyllium
seed

Glossary

Benefic: A planet, aspect or influence that has the attributes of helpfulness.

Individuality: The characterization of a person deep within himself.

Malefic: A planet, aspect or influence that has the attributes of a difficult nature.

House: Any one of twelve imaginary sectors of the heavens indicating environmental conditions in a person's life.

Native: One who is endowed with the qualities of a sign or planet being analyzed or discussed.

Personality: The public image that an individual gives of himself.

Portents: An indication of things about to happen.

Ruling planet: The heavenly body having the greatest amount of influence upon a person or situation.

Sign: One of twelve thirty-degree divisions of the zodiac.

Zodiac: A hypothetical oval-shaped belt containing the larger planets some eight degrees on each side of the path of the sun.

Bibliography
and Suggestions for
Further Reading

Adams, E., *Astrology for Everyone*
Cato, *On Agriculture*
Chatelherault, E., *You and Your Stars*
Culpeper, *Complete Herbal*
Cumont, F., *Astrology and Religion Among the Greeks and Romans*
Dinges, R. L., *Food Education*
Eisler, R., *The Royal Art of Astrology*
George, L., *Horoscope—A to Z*
Heindel, M., *Simplified Scientific Astrology*
Hone, M. E., *The Modern Textbook of Astrology*
James, E. O., *Prehistoric Religion*
Jones, M. E., *Occult Philosophy*
King, H. C., *The Background of Astronomy*
Lewi, G., *Astrology for the Millions*
Lewi, G., *Heaven Knows Best*
Leyel, C. F., *The Magic of Herbs*
Lilley, W., *Astrology*
Lyndoe, E., *Astrology for Everyone*
Mariposa, *Hollywood Cook Book*
McCaffery, E., *Astrology—Its History and Influence in the Western
    World*
Meyer, J. E., *The Herbalist*
Morrish, F., *Outline of Astro-Psychology*
Ptolemy, *Tetrabiblos*
Read, J., *Through Alchemy to Chemistry*
Righter, C., *Astrology and You*
Robson, V. E., *The Fixed Stars and Constellations in Astrology*
Stillman, J. M., *The Story of Alchemy and Early Chemistry*
Theophrastus, *Enquiry into Plants*
Wills, L., *Importance of Herbs in Your Diet*
Wills, L., *Astrological Herbs and Minerals*
Wootton, A. C., *Chronicles of Pharmacy*

ABOUT THE AUTHOR

CARROLL RIGHTER was a protégé of the famous astrologer Evangeline Adams. He is the personal astrologer of numerous celebrities, including bankers, actors, TV stars, political figures and businessmen. He has been a professional astrologian since 1939. He appears daily in hundreds of newspapers, lectures widely, and appears often on television. Mr. Righter lives in Hollywood and is the founder of the Carroll Righter Astrological Foundation.